Walking with Jesus

Published in 2009 by
New Life Publishing, Luton,
Bedfordshire LU4 9HG

© 2009 Maureen Clarke

British Library Cataloguing in Publication Data
A catalogue record for this book is available
from the British Library

ISBN   978 1 903623 39 8

Scripture quotations are taken
from various versions of the Bible
and are used by permission

Typesetting by New Life Publishing, Luton

Walking with Jesus

Maureen Clarke

published by
New life Publishing
Luton, Beds, UK

CONTENTS

continued.......

.... contents continued

*I dedicate this book
to the children of
Our Lady's parish
Moss Side*

Introduction

I hope these meditations will 'touch' you as they have me. Although specifically written for children, they have helped me to meet Jesus in a new way, opening me to the Spirit speaking through them to me as I go about my daily life.

The 'This Promise is for You' seminars which I adapted and presented to the children of inner-city Holy Name Primary, led me on to search for a way to keep the children's awareness of the spirit living within them, alive and vibrant.

Through praying the Gospel scenes, I began to support the Gospel stories with a simple descriptive atmosphere whereby the children could picture the reality of the scene and enter into it as active participants. My intention was to aid the children to experience the love, friendship, and forgiveness of Jesus through a personal meditative encounter with Him.

About a hundred 7-11 year olds meet weekly for our

special time with Jesus. Our parish priest, Fr. Pat Deegan, regularly joins us and I wish to thank him for his continued and unfailing support and encouragement.

We joyfully open our hearts to Jesus as we sing our praise songs to Him. This is accompanied by children on percussion instruments, by children moving spontaneously and clapping in time to the music. Ribbons are waved and banners of praise are held on high. Interspersed between our songs, the children individually express spontaneous words of praise and thanks to Jesus.

The children readily adapt to a still and peaceful atmosphere with the lowering of the lights. Their attention is focused on the small altar, on the candles laid out in the shape of a large cross, or on an illustration of the story for the week. Some children prefer to listen with eyes closed. We all enter into the meditation in our own personal way, letting Jesus touch us as He will.

Following the meditation we pray as community, our prayer related directly to the message of the reading. Then in silence we individually rest for a number of minutes in the presence of the Spirit.

Again we joyfully open our hearts to Jesus as we sing our praises to Him before we all go forth on our separate ways for the weekend.

The Annunciation

Luke 1: (26–35 & 38)

In a small house in a town called Nazareth, Mary is busy attending to her jobs. As she works, she gently sings her praises to God. Everything she does, whether dusting and cleaning, cooking or sewing, she does with a cheerful heart because she loves God and she knows he loves her. It's just an ordinary day for Mary... later, she'll maybe meet her friends, maybe sit in the shade of the trees or maybe go for a walk around the town.

As Mary praises and thanks God she suddenly stands still... rigid. She's aware of someone standing there... she thought she was alone in the house... as she turns she's shocked and feels the colour drain from her face for standing looking at her is something she's never ever seen before... and as Mary stares she just knows it's an angel... she stares in wonder at this part of God's creation she sees for the very first time... she stares and is aware of his gentleness... his calmness... his beauty... and she knows he is all goodness... but she feels a flutter in her chest... her breathing quickens and she begins to fear as she quickly looks round her home... looks at everything she knows so well and wonders is this real... is there really an angel here in the middle of her little home... in the middle of her ordinary day... in the middle of her life. And as Mary hears the angel say:

"Hail, full of grace, the Lord is with you"... she takes a deep intake of breath... no-one has ever spoken to her like that before... she knows God is with her in her daily life but she wonders what all this can be about... she covers her face with her hands... tries to bring her mind back to her ordinary day wondering if this is a dream but this extra-ordinary message from the angel disturbs her and draws her eyes back towards him. Her eyes question... 'Why have you come here?... What do you want?'... and as she gives a little tremble of fear the angel knows and understands, for he says,

"Don't be afraid, Mary"... and the words 'Don't be afraid'... spoken so gently fill and calm her mind and the word 'Mary' spoken with such warmth spreads this very warmth through her... and her fear is drowned by the love flowing from the angel.

The angel moves slowly towards Mary... letting her see the goodwill in his eyes... letting her relax as she sees his truly welcoming expression of face. Mary senses something special in the angel's face... it remains constantly kind and assuring. She knows something special is happening... something special coming to her from God, for this is God's angel... and she waits. Gently the angel tells her,

"You have found favour with God"... Mary wonders why God is particularly pleased with her. Mary wonders why God specially approves of her. Then little surges of fear go through her... she finds it hard, for... she experiences only goodness coming to her from the angel but she also experiences little fears coming from inside herself... fears of not understanding... fears of not knowing why God sends his angel to tell her she is so special to him. The angel beckons Mary to sit... and close by her he too sits. He opens his arms and gently delivers God's message to Mary, God's plan for her.

"You will bear a son"... and he bends his arms together, rocking them as if cradling a baby. Mary imagines a tiny cuddly baby and she smiles. She imagines stroking its soft smooth cheeks... drying its tears... protecting it in her arms... snuggling it up warm and cosy for the night... and she feels a special love stirring inside her... the angel continues... *"...you shall call him Jesus. He will be great and will be called the Son of the Most High God... and his kingdom will never end."* ...but then Mary's eyes, deep pools of gentle love... change to eyes full of questions as she wonders how this can all happen... and how can she, Mary, be such a good and special mother to God's very own son... and her eyes plead with the angel as if saying, 'Who, me?' ...and the angel nods his head in silent answer letting

her know, 'Yes... you'. And his eyes encourage her, fill her with confidence.

He tells her how God will make it all possible. He tells her that the Holy Spirit will live within her and God the creator will live all around her. Mary sits and lets the angel's words sink into her mind... the Holy Spirit in her... God's power around her... and she feels cared for... comforted... filled and surrounded by goodness and love... and her spirit is lifted... she is happy. Mary smiles... she knows God has chosen her to be the mother of his Son and as Mary looks to the angel her mind and heart bubble over with a YES... yes, she wants to do what God wants of her. A peace flows over her... a joy flows over her... she puts herself into God's hands... she trusts him to take care of her... to give her all she needs to be a good mother to his Son.

PRAYER:

Mary was special to God and was chosen as his special helper.

We are special to God and he chooses us as his special helpers too.

Close your eyes and put a picture of Mary smiling at the angel as she says that 'Yes' she wants to do what God wants her to do... to be the mother of His son... and because of Mary's 'Yes', Jesus came to us... came to show us what God wants US to do.

Lord, help us to say 'Yes' to you too.

Mary listened to the angel...help us to listen to You through our priest, our parents, friends and teachers.

Mary chose to say 'Yes'. Each time I choose to be kind, to share, to respect, to be good, I'm saying 'Yes' to you.

Come Lord Jesus come... fill me with your strength... your power... your courage to say 'Yes'.

Come Lord Jesus come *(together)*. Know that through His Spirit Jesus is with you. We praise and thank you Lord God. Amen.

Birds of the Air...
Flowers of the Field

Matthew 6: (26-34)

Note: Provide individual pictures of birds and flowers

And the little child, seeing flowers dancing and swaying on the soil of the earth, kneels before their splendour and gently cups a flower in his hands... wondering..

"Who guides you through the cold dark earth to reach the light?
Who gives water to your roots that you may feed?
Who draws you to stand tall and proud, gleaming in the sun?"

He asks... "Who helps you to grow in beauty?" ... and he understands... because God made the flowers and He does all things good for them so that they grow to become the beautiful flowers that He wants them to be.

And the little child hearing the song of the birds, raises his eyes to the birds that fly in the sky… and he wonders…
"Who guides you to feed on the worm from soil, insect from tree?
Who calls for your song of joy to burst forth with the dawning of each new day?
Who holds you aloft, suspended in the clear, calm skies?"

He asks…"Who looks after you?"… and he understands… because God made the birds and He does all things good for them so that they grow to become the lively, carefree birds of the sky that He wants them to be…

..and as He went from place to place, Jesus watched the flowers dancing happily in the fields… just being themselves with their God-given beauty. Jesus watched the birds joyfully gliding in the air… and watched them working hard to feed their young… just being themselves with their God-given skills… and Jesus was happy.

…and Jesus watched people… but saw worry on their faces… saw discontent in their eyes… unhappiness in their hearts. He didn't want to see them like that… He wanted to help them to be themselves with their God-given skills.

This is how he helped them… He asked them to think about the birds and the flowers and we'll do exactly that too…

(Answer these questions for yourself in your mind)
Have you ever seen birds having to plant, grow and store their food?

Have you ever seen birds worry about what they'll eat tomorrow?

Who makes sure their food supply never runs out?

And Jesus said to the people, **"Your Father in heaven takes care of them. Aren't you worth much more than birds?"**

Have you ever seen flowers work or make clothes for themselves?

Have you ever seen even the richest of kings clothed as beautifully as just one small flower?

And Jesus said to the people that even though flowers only **last a short while, "It is God who clothes the wild grass...so won't He be all the more sure to clothe you?"**

And the people were happy. They understood that they didn't have to worry any more, for Jesus told them,

"Your Father in heaven knows you need things".

They thought of the hardworking and carefree birds....being just what God wants them to be. They thought of the beautiful flowers....being just what God wants them to be and the people thought about how God takes care of each one of them so they can be who He wants them to be.

And the people were happy... they didn't need to worry anymore for they trusted that God would care for them forever and ever.

PRAYER:

Lord, you didn't worry…you trusted the Father to give you everything you needed to do His work. Help me to trust that I will be given everything I need too. Come Lord Jesus, help me to trust. Come Lord Jesus come *(together)*

Come Lord Jesus, help me be the child I'm meant to be. Come Lord Jesus come *(together)*

Lord, with you in my mind and heart I can work hard and be carefree just like the birds. I can show your beauty to other people…just like the flowers and you'll be there caring for me. Come Lord Jesus come… fill my mind and heart. Come Lord Jesus come *(together)*.

The Baptism of Jesus

Matthew 3: (16-17)

Note: As seen through the eyes of a bystander

There's a large group of people excitedly chattering and all facing John the Baptist in the river. I ask around and someone says they've come to be baptised... they want to be forgiven and make a new start.

As I glance over to John the Baptist in the water, I see a man next to him. He too is smiling but his smile is bigger... his smile lights up his eyes... his whole face is peaceful and calm.

Someone tells me its Jesus and its his turn to be baptised. ...I don't know who he is but as I look back at him I see him looking at me and giving me a smile that kind of tells me he's pleased I'm here. I decide to stand around a while longer. I'm interested to know why these people all seem so happy.

I watch John the Baptist. I see him praying. I see Jesus lower his head as if he prays too. I see John place his hand on Jesus' head and lightly press him down to just under the water... and people say that Jesus has been Baptised.

The people around me quieten... there's silence... all is still. I'm drawn to this atmosphere around me... this atmosphere of peace and calm. There's something special going on here... I don't know what it is but I just know I want to stay with it a while longer... I want more of it.

...and then the formation of a shape hovers above Jesus. Against the deep blue of the sky, the sun illuminates the shape and I see a softly feathered dove with its head lowered towards Jesus. I'm unable to move... unable to think. Its pure whiteness sends a delicate reflection of light around Jesus and over the river. The slow opening and closing of its wings seem to send out breaths of gentleness. The fragile feathers catching and lifting slightly in the breeze seem to send out breaths of peace... getting deeper and deeper with each lift of feather... it reaches me... it touches me and I know this is the peace and calm I'd wanted inside me...

I look at Jesus and know something has come to him... I can't see it but I know it has come and it's good... and then I hear a mighty voice... it echoes across the water... but it's a warm voice full of feeling. Jesus' face broadens into a smile... his eyes are radiant and he concentrates as he hears, **"This is my beloved son; with whom I am well**

pleased". Jesus raises his arms in thanksgiving.

Yes, something special did happen and I was included, I was part of it. I know that what I heard were... God's words to his son... the one who did not need to be forgiven in Baptism but the one who chose to be baptised along with all of us... one of us ...and God has come right to this place... this river where I now find myself desperately wanting to be Baptised... and as I am Baptised...

I stand and know I want to be forgiven...
I stand and know I want to make a new start...
I stand and know that I truly smile in happiness and joy... for it is here that I stand and know I am loved... for I believe that God says to me too,
'Ezic, you are my beloved son ... I am pleased with you'.

These words are for you too... 2000 years later... the living God says them to you because he loves you.
I've been changed... I'm part of God's family, sharing my talents... helping my friends... I love and am loved.

PRAYER:
Now put your own name before the words from the Father... "   *(Name)*   you are my beloved child.. I am pleased with you"

Think of him saying this to you now. He says it specially to you, his special child because he loves you. Repeat it a few times in your mind. He wants to say this to you so many times during the day... welcome the Father into your mind so he can tell you what he wants you to know... that he has very special love for you.

....you are my
beloved child.
I am pleased
with you.

The Woman who Touched Jesus' Cloak

Mark 5: (25–34)

It's been twelve long years now since I became poorly. I've tried everything to get well and no doctor has been able to help me. I often hear them talk about how a man called Jesus heals people. I imagine myself well again... imagine being a part of, and having a share in, the life that goes on around me. Nothing and no-one has helped me so far and now I turn to Jesus.

As I stand in my doorway, I hear the crowd following Jesus. I think... 'I must do everything to get myself to Jesus. He can help me'. With head held low and arms holding my shawl tightly round me, I keep thinking about Jesus as I follow along on the fringe of the crowd wondering what to do. Determination to get to Him rises in me... I can't miss Him... He's my only hope. With every step he takes... I take two. When I see a gap, I slide myself into it... I twist and turn through the crowd trying not to touch anyone. I don't want to brush against them in case they're made 'unclean' by my illness, in case they catch my illness, so becoming lonely and isolated like me.

I carefully weave my way towards Jesus... but, as I reach Him, I panic... here is Jesus, the very one who can heal me, I'm so near Him... but how can I step in His path... stop the crowd... announce my pain? As I look down, I see His cloak lifting slightly in the breeze with every step He takes... and knowing that this man, the Saviour, can heal me I believe deep in my heart that,

"If I touch even His clothes, I shall be made well".
...and as his movement and the breeze lift his cloak backwards towards me, I turn the palms of my hands towards Him... and silently send my plea to Him, 'Jesus, Jesus I come to you'. Extending two trembling fingers... I ever so gently touch the hem of His cloak, just the hem, ...I hardly feel the cloth for my touch is so light and doesn't linger... but... I brushed my fingers against His cloak... connected myself to Jesus... linked myself to Him... me, the needy one encountering... meeting... the one who can heal.

Even before I am able to rapidly withdraw my hand back to myself... Jesus suddenly stops walking, everyone stops. Everyone's eyes are on Him wondering why He stops... why He turns to look behind Him... wondering why He stares as if reading the expression on the faces of those following Him... why His gaze rests and burrows deeply into the eyes of those who are now face to face with Him... but I know why... I gasp in shock at my action but my belief in Him led me to do it... and He asks,

"Who touched my clothes?" ...and I start to shake. The disciples wonder what He means... but I know what He means. The disciples let Him know that people have been brushing against Him all the while and say, **"You see the crowd pressing against you and yet you say 'Who touched me?'** ...but Jesus continues to look into our eyes and I lower my eyes from His gaze for my eyes might show it was me... and trembling I don't know whether to stay or run. Have I made Him 'unclean' by my touch... how can I tell Him why I touched Him? As I sink in fear I'm aware of things changing in me... aware of my body feeling better... and I know I'm beginning to be healed... and I know that Jesus knew that someone in need had touched His cloak ...and I know that Jesus experienced the force of His healing power surge out from Him to the one who's fingers touched His cloak... So, slowly, slowly... I move one foot and then another and I raise my eyes back to His and...

"Come in fear and trembling... to... kneel at His feet". I try to speak but my mouth dries up... but as I see the love in His eyes, the concern on His face...I tell Him the whole truth... and as I speak Jesus looks at me... as someone who really matters to Him... and my fear flows away. This is all I had to bring Him – my tiny touch... but with it a faith that He would heal all that this tiny touch brought with it. He tells me, **"Daughter, your faith has made you well; go in**

peace and be healed of your trouble". My faith, my belief in Him led me to Him... through my faith His power reached me... gave me healing... gave me new life. He has made me clean, made me well by His love... His power.

PRAYER:
Dear Lord, the woman believed that you would heal her.

There are times when I hurt badly...
when I feel alone
when I can't do my work
when I can't find anyone to play with
when I'm in trouble, poorly or afraid...
Come now to Jesus like the woman did...
You are his special child... He wants to help you...
Jesus will help you like He helped the woman...
Spend some time quietly with Jesus... just you and Him.

Come, Lord Jesus, come *(say together)* Amen.

Jairus' Daughter

Mark 5: (21-4)

For days my daughter hasn't played with her friends. I can't even tempt her to eat her favourite meal. She slowly makes her way to bed and her little body tosses and turns in pain. Her hair clings to her damp forehead. I think, 'Tomorrow she'll feel better', but as tomorrow dawns I stand looking at her and see that she's worse – she doesn't recognise me. I take her into my arms and beg her to be well. My tears fall onto her face but as they roll over her cheeks I realise that that is the only movement I see… and I know my little girl is very ill.

She needs Jesus. I dash from the house shouting to any-one I see. "Where's Jesus. Have you seen him?" Children playing in the dust just stop and stare at me. People shake their heads unable to help me. I gasp for breath as I run all over the town. Then I see lots of people gathered together and I think 'He's just got to be there'. Everyone's so calm but I dart around the group with a frantic look on my face, bumping into people and apologising but they seem to understand.

I've got to find him and as I clamber to the front of the group I see a man watching me… a man completely at peace… and I just know that this is Jesus. The look of love and understanding on his face just draws me towards him and as I reach him I stand awhile… I look into his eyes for I know that this man is waiting for ME, waiting to help ME, wanting to help ME.

Then I desperately cry out to him,
"Jesus my daughter is very ill. Please come and place your hands on her so that she will get better and live"…
… but then breathless messengers arrive saying,
"Your daughter has died".
… and as my body freezes with shock Jesus reaches out his arms to me… With authority He tells me,
"Don't be afraid, only believe".   …and I do just that.

As he turns I follow him for I have put my poorly daughter into his care and it's only through his power that she can be helped. He leads me along the dusty roads to my home. All the while we're silent… words aren't needed… being with Jesus is enough. I sense his love and understanding flowing into me and I trust him.

As we enter my daughter's room I hear my family crying. I see their sad faces… but as I look to Jesus he is smiling…

he's smiling at my daughter. He moves quietly to her side and ever so gently lifts her hand into his saying with authority,

"Little girl, I tell you to get up"…
…..and at his touch his healing power lights her pale skin with a healthy glow …and she moves. We breath a sigh of relief …and tears, but now of joy, begin to fall. Her eyes flutter open and she knows its Jesus because I see her smile at him …and I smile at him too. His healing power lights MY mind and heart… and all my fear and upset has been made better… Jesus has healed me too and I am filled with joy.

Jesus watches her with love as she gets up and He knows exactly what she needs, saying,

"Give her something to eat".
Now my joy overflows as I see her enjoy her favourite meal.

With praise and thanks on our lips we see Jesus smile at us. Then he turns to continue to bring his love and healing to others.

And this is my true story specially for you. What Jesus did for us he does for you too. Look to Jesus and believe its only him who can do the impossible for you as he did for us.

Close your eyes or look to the picture.
Is there something you've tried and tried to do but can't do it? Jesus can do it.

Is there someone you've tried and tried to help but can't help? Jesus can do it.

Maybe you could tell Jesus... tell Him how you need His help.

As it was for Jairus so it is for you:
Jesus is WAITING for you.
Jesus is WAITING to help you through his spirit.
Jesus is WANTING to help you through his spirit.

PRAYER:
Lord you helped Jairus' daughter and you help me too.
Thank you for being there for me.
I praise you Lord.

LAZARUS

John: 11 (3, 20-22, 35-27, 33-36, 38-44)

My best friends Martha and Mary are desperately upset. Their brother is seriously ill. They send a message to Jesus,

"Lord, your dear friend is ill" ...and they wait for Jesus... waiting with their sadness... their tears and pain. Martha can't sit still. She's up and down to the door all day saying that Jesus will be here soon. Mary huddles in a corner... not speaking... just crying... and they wait. As she goes to the door yet again, I hear her desperate tone of voice as she looks into the distance saying that Jesus has never let her down so why hasn't he come. Nothing will help Martha... nothing but him... nothing till she sees him. I try to help her but her sadness is stronger than my words. It fills her mind and drowns out my words of comfort.

As Jesus approaches, Martha rushes out to meet him, her words tumbling out to him,

"If you had been here Lord my brother would not have died" ...as if she meant to say, 'If only you'd come sooner. I wanted you to come straight away but now you've come too late... you could have made him better if you came when I sent for you'. As she looks into Jesus' eyes she stops and is reminded of who this man is... she is reminded of his love for her... for Lazarus... his power to heal and forgive. I see her body relax... her face soften to stillness and her eyes rest peacefully on the face of Jesus as she says,

"But I know that even now God will give you whatever you ask him for" ...and her own words of faith draw her back to Jesus... and Martha knows that this is the person, who has come from the Father, right into her sadness, wanting to show her who he is... what he wants to do for Lazarus... for her... and Martha believes...

Martha excitedly tells Mary that Jesus has come. Mary rushes out with her friends to meet him and falls at his feet. There's no movement... no sound... but a silence... a silence louder than any words... a silence overflowing with sadness as their tears fall from pools of deep grief. I see Jesus' face descend into sadness... he joins them, feeling what they feel. Steadily tears fall over Jesus' face... he doesn't wipe them away... he lets them fall like those of his friends... in silence he stands with his feelings like those of his friends... and here is Jesus in tears... a human like us... crying like us... and here is our God... knowing understanding and experiencing pain for us, his children, with us as we hurt... And Jesus asks,

"Where have you buried him?" **"Come and see, Lord"** they answer. ...but as they reach the tomb where Lazarus lies their sorrow rises... fresh tears gush forth. Jesus commands firmly and with authority,

"Take the stone away"...but Martha is surprised and tells Jesus that because Lazarus has been in the tomb for four days there will be a smell. And Jesus' eyes beckon Martha and Mary as if saying 'Come and see...' They fall to their knees as they hear Jesus command,

"Lazarus come out". Every breath is held. Every body is still. Every voice is silent. Every eye looks to the tomb. Echoes of movement are heard in the tomb... dragging sounds... shuffles... and there Lazarus stands at the mouth of the dark tomb, illuminated by the sunlight streaming down onto the white bandages of his burial. They stare with shocked, amazed faces but with absolute joy. They came and they saw... and the glory of the Father is shown before them... Jesus tells them,

"Untie him and let him go".
They jump into action helping Jesus to complete the miracle he performed... helping Jesus to show the glory of the Father as they unwrap the bandages to reveal Lazarus alive and well. Jesus came right into Lazarus' sad darkness and lifted him, freed him, resurrected him to the light of life again.

PRAYER:

Place a picture of the tomb in your mind. At the tomb Lazarus needs your help. You're there as Jesus asks you to help him. You're helping Jesus show the glory of the Father.... helping him with this miracle.

Lord, I want to help you by showing your glory to my friends...
Your glory is shown when I smile at a sad person.
Your glory is shown when I go to person who is left out.
Your glory is shown when I say sorry and mean it.
Your glory is shown when I sing my praises to you.
Your glory is shown when I choose to be like you, to my friends.
Your glory is shown when I see someone in need and I try to help them.
Through your Spirit you are living in me....help me to let your glory shine in and around me. Come Lord Jesus come. *(say together)* Amen.

The Temptations of Jesus

Matthew 4: (1–11)

After Jesus' Baptism the Spirit led him into the wilderness to be alone.... to think what it means to be God's son. And in this wilderness... no people... nothing growing... no life... crumbling, hard sharp rocks... dark angry looking hills... rough pebbles and patches of dry sand going on as if forever... And, as night falls... the moon sends eerie shadows which seem to shiver in the intense biting cold of the night.... and as the sun rises the deep heat of the day dances on the surface as if searching to burn away any drop of moisture....

...and from the rocks where I stand, I see you Jesus, in this place... unwashed, covered in dust... your robe torn and trailing behind you... your face drenched in sweat and smeared with dirt... your lips... dry... cracked... needing water to moisten them... and you are my God... enduring the loneliness, the hunger, the weaknesses of your body... struggling on day after day, through love for the Father and for me.

PRAYER:
Dear Jesus, I see you in this grey, lifeless, unfriendly place and I'm sorry for you. You show me that you know all about feeling hurt... so you understand my hurts. Thank you for your understanding Lord.

..and after 40 days and 40 nights alone in the wilderness... I see you, true God and true man, stumble with exhaustion... I see your body drooping... your skin pale... your hair matted and tangled around your face... and your feet... I see the cuts and sores on them from the harshness of the stones you walk upon.

PRAYER:
Dear Jesus I'm with you here and seeing what you go through saddens me.   Then I think, dear Lord, how much more you know how I feel, how much more you are with me, helping me when I too have hard times. I thank you Lord.

...and thoughts rise in your mind
"If you are God's Son, order these stones to turn into bread".
...and you look at the hard, cold stones around you... and in your hunger... you are tempted into thinking...

'My weak aching body cries out for food and I can imagine satisfying, fresh bread all around me'.

...and you are put to the test... and you have choice... choice over your thoughts, over your actions...

...And I see you Jesus, slowly raise your troubled eyes... your dry parched mouth moves to form words... and I know you talk to the Father... trusting him with your struggle. I see your drooping body straighten... your face liven for you have made your choice and you say.

"The scripture says, 'Human beings cannot live on bread alone but need every word that God speaks'. "

PRAYER:
Lord I'm sorry to see you so hungry. Thank you for going through all this before me. It was a struggle for you, so you know it's a struggle for me when I'm tempted. Come Lord Jesus come... I know you are there to help me.

...And pictures rise in your mind...you see yourself on the very highest point of the temple in Jerusalem... and thoughts rise in your mind,

" If you are God's Son, throw yourself down, for scripture says: 'God will give orders to his angels about you; they will hold you up with their hands, so that not even your feet will be hurt on the stones'. "

...and as you seemingly look down from the highest point... you are tempted... and the tempting thoughts in your mind lead you to consider:

'Everyone would follow me, knowing I'm the Son of God, through seeing an amazing display of God's power in rescuing me.'

and you are put to the test... and you have choice... choice over your thoughts

...And I see you Jesus, raise your now thin, weak arms on high...and I know you seek the strength of the Spirit... and you lower your aching head into your hands as if to hold your struggling thoughts... but slowly I see you rise... your body renewed... your thoughts clear... the Spirit with you for you have made your choice saying,

"But the scripture also says, 'Do not put the Lord your God to the test'."

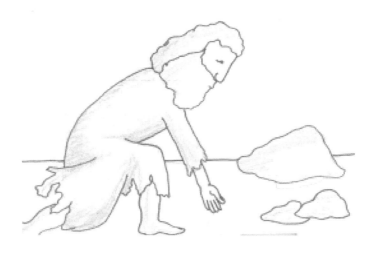

PRAYER:
Lord, I'm sorry for giving into temptation and choosing to use my talents and power for myself, so I get attention and admiration. Thank you for showing me how to choose to use what you have given me to help and serve others. Come Lord Jesus come. I know you are there to help me.

And pictures rise in your mind... you see yourself on a very high mountain looking to all the lands of the world... mountains and valleys... rivers and oceans... the forests... the shores... but the enemy of God offers,

"All this I will give you if you kneel down and worship me".
....and as you view the beauty... the wonders of the earth... you are tempted... and you imagine the importance... the power... the greatness that would go with this... .and... you are put to the test... and you have choice over your thoughts and actions. And to this temptation you firmly shout,

"Go away" ...and in strength and belief you announce,

"The scripture says, 'Worship the Lord your God and serve only him'." ..."**And the angels came to help him"** and to strengthen him to carry out his good choices.

We praise and thank you Lord.

Palm Sunday

Matthew 21: (1-11)

And some people listen to Jesus… some people change their ways… some people know that Jesus is the king of love... the king of peace… and they welcome Him into their hearts, their lives… and they know joy… but Jesus knows there are people who do not yet understand… unhappy people, pained people, lonely people... so many people not yet knowing that He is here specially for them… and Jesus wants to show them… Jesus wants them to see… to see with their own eyes what kind of a king He is.

So Jesus makes His way to Jerusalem knowing that gathered here to celebrate the Passover are many of the very people He wants to help. And Jesus rides forward on a donkey of peace. Behind Him travel His disciples… joyful, excited that He goes to the city to be welcomed and praised as true king… and Jesus rides forward on a donkey of peace, towards the city…

…but in the city before Him, Jesus knows the authorities, the leaders, do not welcome Him, do not want Him there… just wait for the chance to accuse Him… wait for the chance to hurt Him… courageously, Jesus does not hide but… Jesus rides forward, so that all may see Him…

News of His approach travels fast… those who know and love Him rush to welcome Him… and with the disciples, they take their cloaks from their backs and lay them down upon the stony path before Jesus… and others cut branches from the trees to lay before Him… a welcome for their king… and Jesus triumphantly rides forward… waving and smiling to everyone.

Many others see… many others hear that the Messiah comes… and they join the crowd… and they shout and cheer,

"Hosanna to the son of David. Blessed is the one who comes."
…and Jesus rides forward… calmly, quietly, gently upon the donkey of peace but some do not notice this… they see only what they want to see… for some want a king to use force to get them what they want, to put their world right for them.

They do not see that Jesus does not ride a horse ready for battle as did David. They do not see that instead he rides a humble donkey… a gentle animal of peace… this animal chosen specially as a sign of peace…

...and Jesus rides forward wanting to give peace...
...and the donkey moves forward bearing this peace...

More join the crowd... wondering what this is about...
wanting to be part of it all... their cloaks and branches
sweep through the air to the ground... not knowing why...
not understanding... just joining in with the crowd... and

'Hosanna to the son of David' fills the skies for miles
around... and all the while... the bringer of peace rides
forward... without words but...

...desperately wanting them to see...to see with their own
eyes... that He comes not on the horse of battle... that He
comes upon the gentle donkey of peace...

...desperately wanting them to see... to see with their own
eyes... that He comes not to rule as king from a throne... that
He comes to live as king of peace within their hearts...

...desperately wanting them to see... to see with their own
eyes... that He comes not to attack, destroy or harm...
that He comes to care, to help, to love...

...but many do not think... many do not see... many won't
see... many expect Him to be only who they want Him to
be...

but Jesus rides forward... being only who He is meant to
be...

and because they do not understand, because they do not see... before the week is out... many fill the skies with their cries of... **"Crucify Him"**.

PRAYER:

Put a picture of Jesus riding forward, towards you on the donkey of peace... you're in the crowd... you really want to welcome Him... you lay your cloak... your branch before Him... Jesus looks at you and smiles... Jesus gives you His peace... His peace specially for you, His beloved child.

Lord, as I sit here in your presence this afternoon, you want to give me your peace.
Come Lord Jesus come, fill me with your peace.
(together) Come Lord Jesus come, fill me with your peace.

Lord, sometimes I join in with a crowd of friends who are not thinking... not seeing... not understanding that they're being unkind... disrespectful... hurtful.

Lord, I'm sorry. Help me to be brave and not join in even though I may be left on my own. 'Come Lord Jesus come'... help me to be strong enough to stand back from the crowd when it's the right thing to do.

'Come Lord Jesus come'. *(together)* Amen.

The Presentation

Luke 2: (22-33 & 35-38)

It's such a special day for baby Jesus. We're going to the temple to present Him to God. As I carry Jesus to the temple I'm so happy and Joseph's smile tells me how pleased he is with his little family.

Simeon greets us at the temple. Simeon has a peaceful-ness about him because he spends his time quietly in God's presence... worshipping and talking to Him. As Simeon takes Jesus into his arms, his whole face seems to light up with joy. He hugs Jesus closely to himself all the while saying over and over again 'I thank you God... I thank you'. As he strokes Jesus' soft hair and gently runs a finger over his little cheek, I feel so happy that my new baby is loved by this good, kind man. Quietly he speaks to Jesus, saying that the Holy Spirit has been with him all these years, assuring him, **"He would not die before he had seen the Lord's promised Messiah."**

....but I wonder why Simeon talks to our baby about this. Simeon puts a finger into Jesus' tiny hand and as Jesus squeezes it tightly, Simeon's eyes fill with tears... tears of happiness. Simeon holds Jesus tighter to himself and rests his face close to that of Jesus. I see two faces side by side... the face of a tiny baby in sleep... a little smile over his lips and the face of an old man, with a smile of peace over his lips... and I see a love between the two... and this makes me glad. For minutes they rest together in silence and I sense a peace between the two... and this makes me glad.

He whispers to Jesus that today, he just knew that the Holy Spirit was guiding him to come to the temple. Joseph looks puzzled and I don't understand why he says this to a little baby. Simeon then whispers to Jesus 'On taking you into my arms, I knew that you were special because you bring God's promise of comfort for his people.'

I want to ask him why he says this about baby Jesus... but Simeon looks up and over our heads and in a firm, strong voice speaks to God, thanking Him over and over and saying, **"With my own eyes I have seen your salvation"** '...for here in my arms I have seen and held the one you sent to be the saviour of the world and now, my prayers have been answered. God has fulfilled his promise'. Joseph and I look at each other with questioning glances... both of us are **"amazed at the things Simeon said....".**

Simeon looks up into my face, just looking, for a long time...

but as I smile at him I see his face take on a sadness. Simeon very quietly and gently tells me that my heart will know great upset and hurt. I cry to Joseph, 'What does this mean...why have we been told this? I know it is to do with Jesus something happening to Him and I fear for Him'.

As Simeon gently places him back into my arms, I wrap my arms protectively around Jesus... not wanting anything to harm Him... I rock Him, covering Him with kisses as tears of fear for Him now fall. I rub my hand gently over his back as if soothing Him through hurt. I cry, 'Who would want to harm Jesus so badly that my heart would know pain?'. Joseph folds his arms around us, concerned for us, wanting to comfort and protect us both.

Anna rushes over to us with a huge smile on her face... she throws her arms wide in front of us and as she looks to Jesus she gives thanks to God for caring and loving his people so much that He sends this baby as saviour of the world.

Anna's an old lady now and a lady who's known so much upset and pain in her life but you'd never know. She's always so cheerful and it's because she talks to God all the time and He helps her all the time. She's like a mum to everyone... so warm and loving when they're hurting... and Anna stands before me at just the right time... for her presence fills me with hope that as God has always strengthened and helped her in her pain... so too will He help and strengthen me when my heart knows pain.

PRAYER:

Simeon never gave up hope… for years he quietly and reverently prayed and waited for the day when God's promise would come true… Anna never gave up hope… she always prayed for strength in her hard times and waited for God's promise of help to come true… and God answered their prayers.

Lord God, like Simeon and Anna I can have hope in you… I can keep on asking you to help me… keep on telling you when things are too hard for me… and your promise to help me will come true.

As we sit quietly in God's presence let us say together 'Come Lord Jesus come'… knowing that God keeps His promise and comes to us now with His loving help and strength to fill our every need… Amen.

Jesus Walks on the Water

Matthew 14: (22-33)

As night falls Jesus tells us to go ahead of him in the boat to the other side of the lake. He needs to be alone to talk to the father. Some of the disciples soon drift off to sleep.

All I hear is the whisper of wind in the far off trees on the shore and the gentle lapping of water as we slice our way over the smooth calm surface.

A little shiver runs down my spine as a cool breeze begins to move over the lake... it plays on the surface of the water to lift tiny waves which sparkle in the moonlight. I'm at peace tonight... I rest with this peace and let it grow in me.

Without warning the playful breeze turns angry... it forces itself down the lake straight for us... and now... ferociously, it takes hold of the boat, twisting and turning it round. The disciples wake... they fall and scramble around on the bottom of the boat in shock and fear. This wild wind terrifies me... I'm lost... I don't know what to do.

As the wind gains strength it surges and whips water into big, black threatening waves which seem to chase down the lake towards us. We wait breathlessly as they crash over us... gripping hold of the sides of the boat as we huddle together. We don't know what to do... just lost in fear... we wait but we don't know what for.

Screams reach through the air... the disciples stare wide-eyed up the lake... I follow their gaze, the source of their screams. The white silhouette of a figure moves towards us on the water. It walks tall and straight... waves and wind don't seem to touch it. Again I hear screams of fear and...

"It's a ghost. It's a ghost".

Immediately and unexpectedly we hear,

 "Courage....it is I. Do not be afraid."

...And I think, 'Can this really be Jesus? Why is he here, walking on the water in the middle of such a windy night?... and I find myself saying,

"Lord, if it's really you, order me to come out on the water to you."
It's as if I'm saying, 'I trust you Jesus but I can't get to

you on my own. So, I'm putting myself into your hands...
your care and if you want to, then you will give me the
power to get to you over the water'. Jesus replies,

"Come".

I keep my eyes on Jesus' eyes as I move to the side of the
boat. I hold on firmly... put one leg over the side... then
the other, till I'm sitting on the side with my feet just
touching the water.

I see Jesus' eyes crease up as he smiles the biggest smile
ever to me... and he chuckles with delight at my efforts.

A feeling of hope raises me to my feet... and I have no fear.
...no THOUGHT of water... wind... or wave.... just
thoughts of Jesus.

.......no SIGHT of water... wind... or wave... just seeing
Jesus and him seeing   me....his eyes as bright as stars, full
of encouragement.

I want to be with Jesus and as I put one foot in front of the
other, I know I'm filled with the power of God to do what is
impossible on my own....and I walk... ....I walk fearlessly
over the water towards Jesus.

BUT... suddenly... I THINK of the wind and my thoughts
move from Jesus.

suddenly... I LOOK to the roaring waves and my eyes move from Jesus.

suddenly... I HEAR the deafening threats of the wind and waves... hear fear... and my trust moves from Jesus...

...and now, as fear is my only thought... my only feeling... I begin to sink.

Water fills my ears and mouth.... and through the mess I'm in, I thrash around in the water spluttering and gurgling...

"Save me Lord"... for my thoughts come back to Jesus and in my need I know I'm lost... lost and sinking without him ...and immediately he reaches out his hand and raises me out of the water... he saves me.

As we both get into the boat the wind fades to stillness and then silence. We praise Jesus... we praise him saying...

"Truly you are the Son of God."

This is my true story for you. Whenever you have a little fear, practice putting Jesus' face into your mind... see him there with you. Keep your eyes on Jesus' eyes... he is helping you. Your little fear can seem to get bigger on your own. With Jesus in your mind, he shares your fear, loves you and your fear gets smaller and smaller.

PRAYER:

Lord you want so much to be with us when we are frightened.

You had such big fears on the cross so you know how we feel now.

You don't want us to feel that way.

You want us to know your peace.

You want us to trust you and call you to us.

We practice welcoming you into our fears for that's where you want to be.

Come Lord Jesus come *(say together)*
Amen.

The Wedding at Cana

John 2: (1-12)

Excitement rushes through me. The whole village is bubbling. Wedding preparations are underway. The guests arrive with smiles and cheerful conversation. I noticed Jesus, Mary, and some of the disciples, arrive a while back. Jesus is really enjoying Himself. He's relaxed and at ease in this ordinary family home.

Suddenly I notice there's no more wine. How could this ever happen at a wedding? I've got to do something but I can't tell the family... they'd feel ashamed and disgraced. Mary, sitting close by, feels my concern. She immediately sees what's wrong... she goes to Jesus and then says,

"Do whatever He tells you," not knowing what He'll do but believing He'll do what's best for us. Jesus comes and says,

"Fill these jars with water."

I stare at him wondering what all this is about. It'll take ages going backwards and forwards to the village well to collect all that water, especially in this heat... and we'll end up soaked to the skin.

As I stare at Jesus, I see amusement in His eyes as if He knows what I'm thinking. We stagger backwards and forwards to the house with the water and Jesus watches us, giving us smiles of encouragement.

Eventually, the huge jars are filled to the top. We look to Jesus waiting for Him to tell us what to do next. Jesus is quiet... His eyes are closed... His hands are upturned. Something tells us to wait quietly with Him. Then Jesus turns to me and says,

"Now draw some water out and take it to the man in charge of the feast."
I'm shocked. "How can I give him a jar of water?" I ask myself... but... I dip a small jar into the fresh, cool, water. I lift some out... and my hand hovers in mid-air. For seconds there's not a movement from any of us... eyes are fixed and stare unblinking at the jar I hold.

Suddenly, a servant yells, "It's wine. It's wine." Eyes move rapidly backwards and forwards... backwards and forwards from Jesus to the wine. Jesus watches our reaction with a huge smile on His face. Still, my hand hovers in mid-air. I stand and stare at the jar I hold... for in my hand I know I hold a miracle... a miracle of water changed to wine... a miracle needing to be shared and passed on to others. Right here in this ordinary village home I know that Jesus changed water into wine.

Right here in this ordinary village home I know that Jesus prevented embarrassment and upset for the family. He saw their need and helped them.

I turn to make my way to the chief water but stop before Jesus and as I look to Him, I know another wondrous thing has happened today...

I know that as I was filling the jars... His presence was filling me with His love. I know that as He changed the water into wine... His presence was changing me... making me new... and from my hands... I silently pass the miracle Jesus performed to the head waiter... and the head waiter, delighted with the rich tasting wine, praises the bridegroom saying,

"You have kept the best wine till now."
...and from the head waiter's hands, the miracle that Jesus performed, passes out and is shared with all the guests... and I see His glory... His power shining in this ordinary village home... and His glory shines through me... for...

as the wedding guests taste the best wine of the day... I share and taste the best of my day... God's love...

PRAYER:

Close your eyes and see yourself helping Jesus... you're putting water into the jars... As you're filling them with water, know Jesus is filling YOU with His love... filling you with His love today.

See yourself holding the water changed to wine... know Jesus is holding you in His hands changing you... changing you today.

Come, Holy Spirit... fill our hearts... send your love... make me new... help me to share you. Come, Holy Spirit
(say together) Amen

Jesus Heals the Crippled Lady

Luke 13: (10–14)

Note: explain that the Sabbath is a day given to God; no work

There's a woman in our village and we all know her well. Sadly, she's been ill for years, even since before I was born. My mum says she's getting worse by the year. You see, her body is all bent over and she can't straighten it. Today on my way to the synagogue I pass her as she plods along leaning heavily on her stick. We say hello and wish each other well.

When I get to the synagogue there's a big crowd there. Not a whisper can be heard except for a strong but warm voice filling the entire synagogue. I notice that everyone's eyes are glued on the speaker.

He seems different because he talks about kindness, love, caring and I like that. This must be Jesus.

My thoughts are interrupted when I hear the familiar tap of stick and the shuffle of feet... I know it's the woman from our village. She stops beside me and I hear her breathing slowing to calmness.

I see her open hand lift upwards and towards Jesus as if she's trying to reach Him but still her head is bent towards the floor.

Quietly now, she shuffles a little way towards him and He stops speaking... I know she thinks "He has seen me" and she tenses up. Maybe she doesn't want to disturb Him.

His eyes are on her and as He looks at her I see a compassion fill His face... an understanding of her pain. Silently He steps towards her... I see her strain with all her might to lift herself to look into His face but she fails.

He gently places His hands on her and I see her relax at His touch. She knows He cares. He tells her,

"Woman you are free from your illness."
Slowly I see her back rise and straighten... tall and strong. It's as if there had been ropes tied to pull her into a bent position... but now they'd been untied and freed to allow her to straighten up.

Her face becomes fixed on the face of Jesus... His face with its kind loving smile... her face full of praise, gratitude and joy. And there they stand... one with the power to heal ...and one who has been healed. And here I stand...part of it. I see what's happened. I see the tremendous power of God's love and healing working in this woman.

But then the annoyed tone of the leader of the synagogue changes the atmosphere. He booms out that the leaders aren't happy with healing on the Sabbath. I take a deep breath of shock. Something wonderful has happened and now this.

I quickly look to Jesus... He looks serious. He firmly replies that they work on the Sabbath by untying their animals to bring them to water... but... this woman has more need to be untied and freed from her illness... from the pain she's had for 18 years... and the leaders knew Jesus was right.

I look around and everyone is smiling... an atmosphere of peace surrounds me... and I think... what Jesus said and did shows that He never wants anyone to feel hurt and pain.

He will help no matter what day it is, what time it is, day or night... He will help no matter where the hurt is... in the body... in the thoughts or in the heart.

And the woman, tall and straight praises God for His goodness. Because of her, we too know the power of His healing love... this healing love is for us too.

PRAYER:

Sit quietly with Jesus.
Remember what He did for the woman.
Think about the faith she had in Him.
Because He helped her you know He will help you too.
He helps at any time and in any place.
He helps with any hurt, any pain, any fear.
He will help us now.
Call on Jesus... breathe in His healing power...
Let Him help you in the way He wants to.
Come Lord Jesus come

(Say together)... Amen.

The Finding in the Temple

Luke 2: (41-52)

We've been up to Jerusalem to celebrate the Feast of Passover. As we all journey home we realise that no-one has seen Jesus all day. Everyone panics when we realise that Jesus is lost. Mary is so worried and fearful because Jesus is only 12 years old. She imagines Him hurt somewhere... afraid and all alone. Mary and Joseph rush back to Jerusalem to search for Him there.

Their hopes rise as they reach they city but only to fall as they realise that there's just two of them to search this city bustling with people. Mary, in her distress, calls her son by name 'Jesus, Jesus'.... but people ignore her, too busy to even look her way.

Joseph takes her by the arm leading her in their search. They knock on doors. They search building, markets, alleyways trudging through the city hour after hour exhausted and weary till finally they reach the temple.

They stand in the cool dimness of the Temple, clinging to each other as they realise that there is no-where else to search....there is no-where else that Jesus could possibly be.

For minutes they stand, aware that they are not alone for they hear voices in the distance. Making their way in the direction of the voices their eyes widen as they recognise a voice... the voice of a boy... the voice of Jesus.

They rush through the Temple towards Him as tears of relief flood over their cheeks. Their joy at finding Him is overtaken with surprise for there they see their son sitting with the clever teachers of the Temple.

They stop in their tracks as they hear Him discussing God in a way that they themselves do not understand.

Mary and Joseph are **"...astonished..."** as the clever teachers lean towards Jesus and are **"...amazed at his understanding and his answers..."**

Mary is unable to contain herself any longer. She rushes to take hold of Jesus' hands as if never wanting to let go of them again. She senses how happy and calm Jesus is but her worry and fear causes her first words to him to be,

"My son why have you done this to us. Your father and I have been looking for you anxiously."

As Mary says this, she doesn't mean to blame him and Jesus takes no blame but answers her calmly and lovingly with,

"Why did you have to look for me? Didn't you know I must be in my father's house?" for Jesus has begun to understand who He is... a special time for Jesus... a time when He begins to understand that He is the Son of God.

...but Joseph is confused for this house is God's house and Jesus talks of it as **"...my father's house..."** and as Jesus looks into their eyes He knows that they do not **"...understand what He means..."**

but Mary treasures His words in her heart as she remembers those other treasured words in her heart, **"You will bear a son... He will be called the Son of God."**

As Jesus takes Mary and Joseph into His arms,
He knows that His Father chose them to be His parents...
He knows that His Father wants Him to be obedient to them...
He knows that His Father wants Him to return home with them...
He knows that His Father wants Him to continue to grow up in an ordinary home, in an ordinary place, with ordinary friends just like we do.

PRAYER:

Lord, you grew up in a family like we do. You helped Mary and Joseph... you played with your friends... you joined in with everything that was going on. Lord, you loved your parents and were obedient to them by accepting their love and guidance, advice and support.

Put a picture of your family into your mind... see yourself there with them... they have been chosen specially to help you to grow into the good person you are meant to be Lord, I love my family... help me to be obedient to them by accepting their love and guidance, advice and support.

Come Lord Jesus come *(together)* ...help me to show my love for my family in a little way tonight... I want to co-operate with everyone at home... I want to help mum when she's tired... I want to be kind to my brothers and sisters...
Come Lord Jesus come.   Amen.

Jesus at the Home
of Simon the Pharisee

Luke 7: (36-38 & 44-50)

I've heard that Jesus is at the home of Simon the Pharisee. I'm not an invited guest but I just have to go to Jesus. I find myself shaking for I shouldn't be here. From where I watch I see Jesus sitting in his clothes of the day.... no finery like the other guests but he's comfortable in their presence. He shows friendliness and it goes deeper than that... it's love. I've done wrong... big wrongs and I need to go to Jesus. I need him to help me... to forgive me.

I'm so ashamed because everyone avoids me because of what I've been like... and I know that Jesus is the only one who can make it right for me. The other person I see is Simon... he moves as if he's very important. He's busy accepting congratulations from everyone for inviting Jesus... but he doesn't seem to spend any time with Jesus.

I just want to turn round and rush off home... I know I won't be welcome here... they know me... know my wrongdoings... in their eyes I am the 'sinner' and will always be the 'sinner'... but deep inside me I don't want to be like that anymore... I want to change... I wish they'd believe me... but no, they still give me looks of disgust and anger... and this makes me feel worse.

I see so many people sitting between me and Jesus and I don't know how to get to him without being seen... but I see Jesus looking at me... his eyes urging me forwards... giving me courage.

To the sides of me I'm aware of heads held high and piercing eyes boring down into me as I move towards Jesus... I tremble and lower my head... an atmosphere of dislike and judgement reaches me from the guests... and I hurt... but the look on Jesus' face says 'Come to me, you are loved'... and he waits for me.

I come and sit near his feet... he knows what I've been like... what I've done wrong. As a sign of my love and my belief in his forgiveness, I come here to put my only treasured possession... my perfumed oil onto his feet. As I silently sit with him... everything bubbles up and flows out to him as tears, falling onto his feet.

These tears carry my sorrow for my wrongdoings... it's as if Jesus holds and bears my sorrow for he doesn't wipe away my tears... and my tears carry my joy and with my tears of joy, I praise and worship him.

I release my hair from its clasp and vaguely hear gasps of shock at my action for no 'good' woman is seen with her hair hanging freely. I smooth my flowing hair over his feet to make them dry... all the while kissing them in honour and respect for him. My love for him is shown as I tenderly place droplets of my oil onto his feet... in silence and stillness I sit at his feet.

The sound of gentle movement eventually reaches me... I look up to see Jesus looking so kindly at Simon... but Simon is glaring at me and I take a deep sharp breath of shock at the look on his face for I feel criticised and unwelcome. Jesus explains to Simon that he did not offer the usual welcome to him as one of his guests.

Simon is shocked and surprised... but now he understands that all he was doing was showing off his wealth and reputation instead of giving love and understanding. Jesus explains that the love I have shown to him is part of my belief in His power to forgive and he says to me,

"Your sins are forgiven. Your faith has saved you; go in peace"

I know that He has saved me from my inability to be good without Him...I become more like Him as he breathes His love and forgiveness in me.

PRAYER:

In your mind look at Jesus as the love flows out to the woman at his feet. That's how he looks at you... and as he forgives her... so he wants to forgive you.

Is there something you want Jesus to forgive in you?
Just tell him.
Tell him you are sorry and want to do better.
Ask him to forgive you.
Ask him to help you to be better.
Come Lord Jesus come. *(say together)*
We thank and praise you Lord. Amen.

Martha and Mary

Luke 10: (38–42)

My face widens into a huge smile and I shriek with excitement as I see who's come to stay with us. My sister Mary and I don't stop chattering as we lead the disciples and our friend Jesus into our home... welcoming them... making them comfortable... seeing to their needs. Jesus chuckles at our excitement.

I'm honoured to have Jesus in our home. I'd like to sit with him... listen to him... learn more from him but I also want to go and make an extra special meal for our special visitor.

I leave Mary with Jesus. As I look back at them, I see her 'sitting at Jesus' feet' listening to his teaching. Her eyes are fixed on his face... she looks so calm and peaceful. Jesus is relaxed and happy. Mary smiles with such love as she listens to his every word.

As I quietly go about my work I'm so aware of Jesus' presence in my home... I think about him... I hear the gentle tones of his voice a little way off... but his voice gets fainter and fainter and my thoughts of him get fainter and fainter as the heat of the day together with the heat of the cooking begins to affect me... I become all hot and bothered.

Some things are taking too long to cook... other things are ready. I worry that the meal will be spoilt. Now I can't find the dishes I need. I begin to get really annoyed. I could do with some help in here.

Mary always helps me but here I am on my own while Mary's sitting there. Surely she'll come in a minute. All I can think about is how she shouldn't leave me to do this on my own.

I feel myself getting angry. I begin to bang the pots down hard... that should let her know I want her here... she'll soon get the message... but no... Mary doesn't appear. I get louder.... banging and crashing everything I touch. I think of nothing else but myself and how I'm left here to deal with all this all on my own... and now I'm angry. I want Mary to do what I've decided she should do.

I march boldly to Jesus and Mary and I say,
"Lord don't you care that my sister has left me to do all the work by myself. Tell her to come and help me".

I stand looking at how calm and happy Mary is... but I stand looking a wreck because I feel a wreck inside me... I'm all chewed up and annoyed. Jesus is looking at me.

"Martha, Martha..." he calls to me... and he tells me, **"You are worried and troubled over many things... but just one thing is needed. Mary has chosen the right thing and it will not be taken away from her."**

I want to ask him what he means but I'm still too full of my own annoyed thoughts. I slowly turn back to my pots and pans and slump down on a stool wondering... wondering so hard what Jesus means...

Yes, I think Jesus is right. All I did was worry about everything and that led me to feel so alone.

Mary didn't let anything, not even my banging around, distract her from Jesus... but I distracted myself from Jesus with my worried and annoyed thoughts and my banging around. Mary spent time with Jesus... listening to Him... learning from Him... getting to know Him better.

So Mary has chosen the better thing to do... she wasn't too busy to be with Jesus.

PRAYER:

As we sit here peacefully and calmly in Jesus' presence, we're spending time with Him just as Mary did.

Close your eyes... see yourself with Jesus. Perhaps you'd like to tell Him how you are.

Perhaps you'd like to praise and thank Jesus for this good week.

Perhaps you want to say sorry for something you've done wrong.

Perhaps you want to sit quietly with Jesus knowing that He's here specially with you... filling you with His love.

Come Lord Jesus come... fill us with your presence.
(say together) Amen.

The Man at the Pool

John 5: (1–8)

Most of my life I've been here because I'm disabled. If I'm first into the pool when the waters bubble up I'll be healed. However, as I slowly and painfully drag myself to the water someone always gets there before me. So, for 38 years now I've watched and waited... night and day... wanting to be first. One day I decided that my life wasn't so bad after all. I don't like being disabled but I'm getting quite used to it here.

I've become weary of trying to drag my body down to the waters when they bubble. So, as I hear cries of 'Hurry, come on. The waters are moving.' I do make the effort but I don't seem to be as enthusiastic about it as I was years ago.

As I lie on my mat watching the comings and goings around me, I notice someone staring hard at me. I bet he knows I'm the worst here and have been here the longest. He'll come over soon, give me loads of sympathy and ask if I need anything. Out of the corner of my eye, I see him approach me and in a firm strong way he says,

"Do you want to get well?"
My head snaps round to face him... I wait for the sympathetic pat on the back... the words I've heard so often that try to assure me that I'll be first to the pool next time... the offer of drink... the assurances of return visits to see and help me... and I wait but he doesn't give this that I want and expect... shock... it just doesn't happen. Instead, I'm shaken up... confused... this man is different... he doesn't look at my crippled body... he looks into my eyes and as he looks I imagine he sees right inside me as if he knows my very thoughts. I don't like this so I close my eyes... seconds later I take another look at him and still his eyes are on me... this man is different.

As I look at him, his face and attitude bear an honesty, a truth. He genuinely wants to know if I want to be better. Avoiding giving an answer I say instead,

"Sir, I've no-one here to put me in the pool when the water is stirred up; while I'm trying somebody else gets there first".
There were many who'd have helped me reach the water if I'd have shouted loud enough. The truth is... I'm frightened of changing... changing from thinking just of myself and what others could do for me... changing from choosing the easy, selfish way of life I made for myself...

changing from a life I know to a way of life I don't know. This man seems to see, to know these thoughts for his face softens. I know he understands me and doesn't blame me... he just seems to accept that this is me.

Now I'm being true and honest I get a really good feeling... much better then the feelings I've had before. Now I have true peace and joy... this man has helped bring it to me. He stands next to me... with me... as I turn   my thoughts around in my head and decide... 'Yes, I do want to be healed'. He knows my answer now... he reads it in me... he knows I really want to be better. I know that he's given me courage... courage to change and to say goodbye to the excuse 'I have no-one to get me to the water'.

...and as he knows this, he speaks to me without the soft sympathetic tone of voice I'm used to receiving but with a firm tone of authority as he tells me exactly what he wants and expects of me,

"Get up, pick up your mat and walk."
I listen and know he means it. Somehow he knows I can do it and I begin to believe I can do it with his help. Immediately, I try to move my stiff painful body... it moves... it works... it carries me and I'm walking... each step I take gets easier, better... and I'm filled with joy. My wanting to be healed together with this man's power has made me new... a miracle. HE walked by, stopped and healed me. He stepped into my hopeless world and gave me hope.

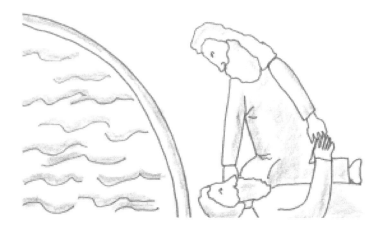

PRAYER:

Put a picture of Jesus' face into your mind.

Jesus is asking you if there is something in you that is hard for you to change.

He wants to do it with you by filling you with His courage and by giving you His healing power just as He did for the man. He wants to be with you helping you to be strong enough to change your ways.

Rest silently with Jesus and let Him fill you with His helping spirit.

Come Lord Jesus come *(say together)*

We praise and thank you Lord

Jesus Appears to the Disciples

John 21: (1–14)

I promised I'd never let Jesus down but I did. I turned away from him saying I didn't know him... I ran away... left him just when he needed me. Now I've returned to the life I knew before I met Jesus... back to my old home, my old job... but I know that this isn't right for me now, not after having known Jesus.

I'm here in my small fishing boat listening to the waves gently lapping against the sides. We're all shivering, tired and hungry after a whole night's fishing and not a fish did we catch.

A dull grey mist lies over the water... a greyness all around me reminding me of the last time I was on my boat. It was the night before my whole life changed... the night before Jesus came and called me to be a 'fisher of people'... and now, all I see is this empty net and I remember the empty net that very night long ago... and it makes me think... that's what wrong with me... I feel empty without Jesus.

As the sun slowly rises, the mist burns away and another new day is born. Slowly the shore comes into view and there stands the figure of a man watching us. He seems friendly for he calls to us questioning,

"Young men, you haven't caught anything?" Someone disappointedly replies, **"Not a thing,"** and then we hear,

"Throw the nets out to the right side of the boat and you will catch some."
My breath catches in my chest ... I stand rigid as I remember hearing similar words before... but, my thoughts are disturbed by the splashing and commotion in the water to the right of me... and we all leap into action. We strain with all our might to haul the net aboard... but our efforts fail for the catch is so heavy we can't lift it... but then I hear a shout,

"It is the Lord."
There he stands on the shore, the shore where I first met him, beaming a huge smile of welcome to us all. I grab my cloak and leap overboard. I just have to get to him.

I excitedly splash my way through the water and as I stagger ashore soaking wet, I see Him chuckle at the sight before Him. As I look at Jesus, I remember the last time I was on my boat and we caught nothing... just like tonight.

As I look at Jesus I remember hearing, **"Let down your nets for a catch"** ...just like I heard today. As I look at Jesus I remember a huge catch... just like today's huge catch. **"Come and eat"** he invites... and I remember that day He invited us to come with Him on His journey.

And as He serves us with food I remember how He bent low in humility and service to wash our feet. And as he takes the bread into His hands I remember the Last Supper.

And as He takes the fish from the fire I remember enough fish to feed five thousand. All these memories I have and the reminders Jesus gives me draw me back to Him... to follow His ways.

At last I forgive myself for leaving Him when He needed me and I, Peter, make a new start to continue my journey with Jesus, carrying Him in my heart wherever my journey takes me.

PRAYER:

Lord, sometimes I'm like Peter... I forget and go and do things my own way.

You never left Peter all alone and no matter what I do you never leave me.

You came to Peter to help him to remember that you love him and you want him to help you.

You come to me through your Spirit to remind me that you love me and you want me to help you.

Sit quietly... just you and Jesus... your special time with Him... no words are needed... just breathe in His Spirit of love... let it fill you... let it remind you that Jesus lives deep within you, always loving you... always with you.

Come Lord Jesus come *(together)*.   Amen.

Jesus Calls the Fishermen

Luke 5: (1-14)

I'm an ordinary fisherman and I just love my job. Some nights the beauty of the water, sky and moon fills me with wonder and peace as I lower the nets and wait in stillness for the fish to fill them. Other nights when the wind and waves are 'angry' I just can't catch my breath with fear and there aren't many fish to catch.

After a particularly disappointing night I sit thoughtfully washing the nets. The shore fills up with excited, eager people... I wonder what's going on. Looking closer, I notice Jesus strolling ahead of the crowd towards me.

With a twinkle in his eye and amusement on his face, he watches my surprise as he climbs into my boat... and then he asks me to push it out a little way into the water. No longer do I sit silently worrying about my work and lack of fish... Jesus needs my boat... he needs me. As I stand beside him in the boat, the breeze carries his voice to the shore... to the people who come to hear him... and I am part of this, for his presence near me stills my worry and seems to fill me with something I've never known before... and it's good. When Jesus turns and says to me,

"Push the boat out further to the deep water and let down your nets for a catch." I know I don't want to start fishing again... I've been on the water all night and there are no fish. So why is he asking us to start all over again? I have a little moan to myself but I do what he says.

Suddenly the nets pull forcefully on the boat... I lose my balance as the boat tilts to one side... overhead birds gather and squawk, circling over the submerged nets... these are the signs of a good catch... I hear the fishermen shouting 'Where have they all come from?' ...I look to Jesus and I see a look of intense happiness on his face... I look around me and realise work needs to be done. We strain and stretch to gather in the nets. We're strong men, used to hard work but this is too much for us. We've never had such a heavy catch before... sweat drips over our faces... our muscles expand with the force of our efforts... we need help. We wave to another boat to come and help us... double the strength... double the man-power and we fill two boats with fish. We fear we'll sink under the weight, so we head for the shore.

'How did it happen?... What's going on?' I ask myself. I soon come to my senses and recognise the power of Jesus at work... making the impossible – possible... empty to full nets. Suddenly, I fall to my knees in front of him and I say, **"...I am a sinful man"** for, I am face to face with my own weaknesses and wrongdoings. And Jesus says, **"Don't be afraid... "** I raise my head to him and see his hands reach out to me. I see forgiveness on his face and love coming out to me, making me new inside me... and he continues, **"...from now on you will be catching people."** Jesus' call to me turns me upside down and I know I'll never be the same again. Jesus wants me to help him to show and give others what he has shown and given to me. He wants me to help to spread this good news everywhere.

There's no way I can turn back to my boats and let Jesus continue his journey without me. I want and need to be with him... but, what can I give him? I'm a tough fisherman... always smelling of fish and the sea... no education... no fame... no success... always talking too much without thinking. I turn away from my boats knowing all I have to give him is a willing heart and mind... and I know this is what he wants. I face Jesus with three of my fishermen friends and we take our first steps with him, knowing we're on a journey with him... maybe peaceful and happy, maybe hard and difficult... but... this journey will be with Jesus walking beside us.

This is my story for you. Jesus did a lot with what I gave him... a lot with just my willingness to serve him. You can read about me in your Bibles today. Jesus kept his promise to me, Peter... I became a 'fisher' of people bringing Jesus to people... and people to Jesus. With Jesus the impossible became possible... I became St. Peter, the first pope... fisherman ... to Jesus' special helper.

PRAYER:

Put a picture of your friend Jesus into your mind. Jesus wants you to choose to follow him like Peter did. Practice following him in little ways... that's what he wants for you. Maybe when you're faced with a tiny situation when you want to get the attention of your friend during a lesson, when you want to answer your teacher or your mum back or when you feel 'meany' towards your friend you could choose instead, to be kind like Jesus is – that is doing it his way, that is how you follow him. Ask Jesus to help you. He is always waiting to help you. Lord, help all of us to choose to follow your way of doing things. We thank and praise you Lord.

Come Lord Jesus come. *(say together)* Amen.

The Shepherds' Story

Luke 2: (8–20)

Note: 'Stand beside the shepherd boy' in this story... be his friend... see what he sees... hear what he hears... do what he does... join him and be with him.

Not long ago I joined my dad and his shepherd friends up on the hilly fields... for I am the new shepherd boy. As I sit round a small fire with the others we chat and laugh about the tricks sheep get up to as they try to wander off on their own... but our chatter dies down... our heads slowly turn... for a pale gentle light begins to form over the deep blackness of the sky. I shout, 'What is it? What is it?' but no-one answers.

We huddle together as if for protection. I hear their deep loud breaths of fear... I hear my own breaths of fear... I feel their trembling bodies against my trembling body ...I smell the odour of sheep... the odour of nervous sweat...

the odour of panic as I bury my face against them.

...but, a beauty faces me... a soft smooth face... clear kind eyes... flowing hair mingling and blending with clothes seemingly made from tones of pale light... so, why am I afraid? I know it can only be an angel and this angel brings no harm. He smiles a smile of kindness, a smile of love... he breathes a gentleness and calmness around him. I see gentle rays of light slowly floating like wispy clouds... coming closer and closer... until... this glorious light is all round us, bathing us in its love, its gentleness.

It's not of our making... it can only be of God... God coming to us silently, in the silence of the night... and I know something glorious is going to happen.

I try to shout 'Why, why?' but my voice makes no sound. My mind can't think as I feel a shudder of fear travel through me again. This can't really be happening... I blink and rub my eyes. I take a tiny peep and yes, this is real... this is true... God's angel is with us. The angel knows we're afraid and shocked. He says with a gentleness and concern for us,

"Do not be afraid. I bring you good news of great joy which will come to all people." His words calm me... but, good news?... What can he mean?... nothing special ever happens up here... we do little but mind the sheep... why would the angel choose us? He goes on to announce to us something wonderful... something the world has been waiting for... something all peoples need and want.

...he tells us that a saviour has been born who is Christ the Lord... We look expectantly at God's messenger... wanting more... knowing he waits to deliver more news. He goes on to tell us how we will recognise the new baby... how we will know where he is,

"....And this will be a sign for you: you will find a babe wrapped in swaddling clothes and lying in a manger." ...our very saviour... this special baby born for all peoples lies in nothing more than a poor manger... and as I ponder this, the skies are gently illuminated... and I stare in wonder and awe at masses of angels robed in delicately flowing garments. Their gentle voices rise to fill the skies with praise... masses of angels united in praise for our God... their praise rising as one voice saying,

"Glory to God in the highest and on earth peace to all people." We go **"with haste"** for this news is all we've longed for. We scramble down from the hills... panting with excitement. We want to meet the saviour... we want to be with him... and, just as the angel directed, just as the angel said... we find him there in a manger... and we fall to our knees in worship of him. Mary smiles knowing we too have received and are bearers of this good news.

I tip-toe towards the manger... I see his little face screw-up and know he has a windy pain just like my little brother... and a tiny tear squeezes from the corner of his eye... I catch and hold it on my finger and think 'He hurts like us... and cries like us'. As I watch his little chest rise and fall with each breath I praise and thank him for who he is... Jesus, our saviour breathing the peace and love of the Father here with us all. As I stroke his soft cheek, his little eyes open and as our eyes meet I know I see our Saviour. I witness... I see for myself the truth of what the angel announced to us... and all who hear it are amazed.

From the depths of our hearts, our voices rise with praise and thanks blending as one voice... the voice of the shepherds united in praise to our God.

Mica

PRAYER:
Father God, you came to ordinary shepherds, on an ordinary night, trusting them with the biggest most important announcement ever to be made in the whole world...

We too have heard this announcement with the shepherds... on this ordinary school day... **"A saviour has been born..."** The shepherds rushed to Jesus... As we sit together *(in the hall)* on this ordinary school day... we come to you... we sing our praises to you just like the shepherds...

Father God, Jesus came to earth and gave the shepherds a joy and peace they'd never known before... Come Lord Jesus come... fill me with your joy and peace.

Come Lord Jesus come *(say together)*   Amen.

The Woman at the Well

John 4: (1–30 & 39–42)

I stumble up the dusty path with my water jar to the well. I'd rather come when it's cooler but that's when the other women come. I always come on my own so that the women won't give me disapproving looks, gossip about me or make me feel different. The other women lead good lives and don't accept me so there's no place for me with them... I don't feel one of them.

Reaching the well, I see a traveller slumped against the wall. He looks exhausted and weary... and in a way, a little sad sitting there all alone in this blazing heat. I just want to draw up my water and get off home but, the silence is broken with, **"Give me a drink"** ....and I stand still not knowing what to do... I feel for him... I can tell his throat is dry and his mouth dusty... he needs water.

But, I can't believe I hear this man do what no Jew does - he talks to a woman in public... I can't believe I hear this man ask what no Jew asks – to share the drinking jar of a Samaritan. So, I ask him straight out,

"How is it that you a Jew, ask a Samaritan for a drink?" ... He moves closer to me and with great earnestness, he says that... if I knew who he was... firstly, I'D ask HIM... and then, HE'D give me water... living water.

He tells me that the water in the well will always leave me thirsty... but, his water flows like a spring... never ever stopping... quenching thirst forever. I don't really understand what he means but I know he's offering me an incredible gift.. his water... fresh, new water that will always be there... water that will give me all I need forever and ever, so that I'll never be thirsty again... and I wonder how this can be?

Why does he tell me this? He smiles and gives me an encouraging look... so, despite not knowing what's going on, despite not understanding how he can give me such water... I say,

"Sir, give me that water. Then I'll never be thirsty again." ...and I think that I'll never have to trudge up to the well struggling with my water jar in this heat anymore.

Then he mentions my husband. I tell him I don't have a husband... quietly, gently he says that I speak the truth... my breath catches in my throat... his eyes, clear and understanding look into mine... I can't turn away. This man, who I've never met before, then tells me all about myself ...my life... my trials... my upsets... my wrongdoings... and I feel the colour drain from my face with shock... only to flush back again burning my cheeks with shame and regret... my body slumps and my head falls into my hands as my body shakes... for this man seems to know me and what I'm like.

He seems to know that my life is a mess... but he doesn't treat me like the women in the village do because of this... he smiles at me... his face relaxed... caring... accepting. I wonder why he's so kind to me, all the while knowing what I'm like?...

My encounter... my meeting with him has saved me from the loneliness... the isolation of my old life, the wrong-doing of my old ways because he promises me a new life of hope, of joy, of love... a fresh new life bubbling inside me... just like a spring of moving, refreshing running water, flowing forever.

I rush to the village forgetting what they think of me there... I just have to tell them of his promise... I have to tell them of his saving power... and they come... they see and hear for themselves and they know that the 'saviour' has come to them, the Samaritans, and they proclaim him "Saviour of the world".

PRAYER:

Lord, the woman said **"Give me that water"** and she was filled with your Spirit... your Spirit giving her everything she'd ever need... your Spirit bubbling up inside her like a never ending spring of water... and she knew peace and joy...

"Give me that water" the woman prayed to Jesus... and Jesus answered her prayer...Perhaps we could say the woman's prayer... make it our prayer too... **"Give me that water"**.

Let's say it together **"Give me that water"** ....and just as he gave it to the woman, he gives it to us too.

We praise and thank you Lord. Amen.

The Centurion's Servant

Matthew 8: (5-1)

I've not slept all night. My servant needs me. As I sit by his bed I try to comfort him. I bathe his forehead and give him tiny sips of water but still he hurts.

He tries to move but can't.
He tries to speak but can't.
His eyes beg me to help him.
Many people have tried but he's just getting worse.
I see how terrified he is.
He knows I care for him and would help him if I could.

The oil-lamp gets lower as I sit by his bed. I don't want him to feel alone. As I sit through the long night with him I know what I'll do as soon as the new day breaks… and as I make this decision my servant sees all the worry and upset disappear from my face. My face tells him that everything will be alright.

As I reach the door I turn and say to him, "I'm going to find Jesus" ...and my servant closes his eyes and falls into a peaceful sleep.

Neither of us has ever met Jesus but we believe he will help us just as he has helped so many others.

I go looking for Jesus. Nothing can stop me. In the distance I see a man with such a kind gentleness on his face that I just know it's him. I rush to his side and as he turns to me he gives me such a welcoming smile that my hurried breath slows down and I become calm in his presence.

I tell him all about my servant and by the way he looks into my eyes I can tell he's carefully listening to me and He says, **"I will heal him"**.

I really, really believe Jesus can help but I say to Him, **"Lord, I am not worthy to have you come under my roof; but only say the word and my servant will be healed."**

I tell Jesus that I believe in my soldiers and know that they will do what I ask of them but my belief that He will do what I ask of Him is so much stronger... that His power and authority is so much richer than mine... and that I believe He is able to make my servant better by just saying the words from here, where He stands.

I see Jesus' eyes widen… he is happy that I have such belief and trust in him ...and as He says the words,

"Go, what you believe has been done for you" ...I know and believe that my servant is now better. As I rush to his side I shout and sing my thanks and praise to Jesus.

We've just entered into this wonderful healing that took place 2000+ years ago.
Jesus is the same today as he was then.
Jesus does the same for us today through his spirit as he did then.

We can meet Jesus just like the Centurion did.
The Centurion ASKED for help.
We can ASK for help for someone we know who is hurting... it might be in their body or in their heart and feelings. We believe Jesus is there waiting to help and waiting for us to ASK for this help.

Let us close our eyes and for a short while meet Jesus. Let us ask for his help. Come Lord Jesus come *(say together)*...

PRAYER:
Lord Jesus, thank you for being there when I call to you.
Thank you for answering my prayer.
I praise you Jesus for all your help.
Amen.

The Blind Man

John 9: (1-7)

So often I sit and wonder what they look like – the trees, the birds, the soft rain falling, the flowers and my family… for I have never seen them… I am blind.

I've always been like this and sometimes it makes me sad. I want to see and enjoy the beauty of the world around me.

Sitting by the wayside and listening to the sounds of the world, I hear in the distance a man's voice that I've never heard before. It's a warm friendly voice. The voice gets closer and I realise the man is standing next to me.

I hear him saying that I am special… that God has chosen ME to let his love and healing power WORK through me… to SHINE through me so that everyone can see it and know it.

I don't know what he means but I feel so calm and I trust this kindly spoken man.

I hear him gather some grains of sandy soil and mix it with his healing spittle. He gently holds my face in his hands as he slowly and carefully covers my eye-lids with the mixture. In the heat of the day it dries hard on my eyes and I can't open them.

He tells me to wash my eyes in the nearby water. I sense he has a purpose in this and he wants me to do my part, to take part in what he is about. He speaks and acts with an authority that is good and kind. It makes me feel safe and secure, so I do what he wants me to do.

As I stumble slowly towards the water I DO wonder what all this is about but I sense that he wants me to trust and believe in him. I do just that.

I wash my eyes and as I open them I see what I've never seen before… shapes… I blink and stare… I realise I see, what can only be a face… a face reflected in the water… and this face is smiling. I slowly move my eyes sideways to another face looking at me from the water… eyes and mouth wide in amazement… I realise that this is my face. My eyes dart backwards and forwards from face to face… I shout: 'I can see. I can see'.

Now I know what love is… I see it on the other face reflected in the water.

Now I know what love is… it has come to me and made me better.

Now I know that this other face can only be that of Jesus.

He came to ME. He came and healed ME.

I see tears for the first time… my own wonderful tears of joy falling from my eyes as I gaze at my very own face in the water.

I turn right round to face Jesus beside me and I see his loving smile as I praise and thank him at the top of my voice.

Then he leaves me.

People don't recognise me because I can now walk tall and straight. They ask me how it happened. I tell them Jesus did it. They want to know where he's gone and I tell them I don't know. BUT I tell them what I DO know: that every time I see a ripple on the water… every time I bathe my face… every time I thank him for my sight… I gather his face into my mind…. that very face reflected in the water and I know that he is with me… and I know I have no fear…

This is my story for you children. Jesus changed my life… he came to me, a blind beggar… he's longing for you to let him help you too. Stop a while and let his healing power and love shine through you too.

Remember that every time you smile you're showing the reflection of the very first smile I ever saw... the loving smile of Jesus. Your smile brings Jesus' goodness and love to others.

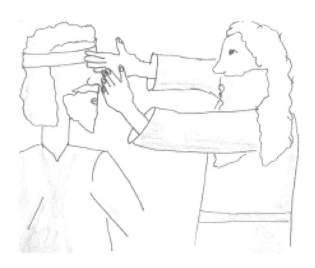

PRAYER:
Put your picture of Jesus' face into your minds.
Welcome him.
Just sit quietly with Jesus as he comes to you.
You are special to him.
He has chosen you.
I praise you Lord for loving me.
Come Lord Jesus come *(say together)*
Amen.

The Leper

Mark 1: (40–45)

Note: For sensitive children, explain that leprosy is not found in the country in which they live.

I don't live with my family. I've got leprosy and its so catching that no-one must touch me. The rule is that I mustn't go near anyone and it makes me sad. As the weeks and months go by I get worse… the sores begin to go deep into my skin and give off an unpleasant smell. I hurt. I find the loneliness hard. My family wants to help but they can't come to me so they get sad.

Now, in the distance, I see a man strolling by. As I peer over the rocks I think that it must be Jesus because he looks so friendly and kind. People are following him, chatting to him… I see him laughing with them. They all look so happy. I want to be with them.

It gets me thinking. I'm so desperate now. I really need help and he's the only one who can help me... but how can I go near him the way I am? Then, his eyes move from the people and turn to look all over the hills. His eyes narrow against the sun. It seems as if He's looking for someone. Does he hear me clumsily plodding around on the stones and pebbles? Has He heard that I live up here?

I know, know, know that I have to go to Jesus. I can't let Him walk right past me. I can't miss Him. I know it's my chance to come out... I see him waiting... his face, his eyes draw me to him. I struggle to reach him and He watches me with a smile.... encouraging me on. He sees me making so much effort... I stand a way off from Him but as he steps towards me, people shuffle backwards, away from me; but not Jesus.

....because of fear I know everyone runs from me
....because of fear no-one wants to know me.
I know I look a mess... but not to Jesus...
He sees me as a person in need.
I know he has the power and love to help me so I say,

"If you want to, you can make me clean from the leprosy."
I want it so much but I don't tell him what to do. I put myself into his care. Then, I feel a tremendous sense of relief because Jesus looks at me with such understanding. He knows and accepts how I feel.

As He moves towards me lifting His hand out to me

everyone gasps, their eyes widen and stare hard... fear ...fear of my leprosy... but Jesus TOUCHES me... and he's SMILING. I fear too that he'll catch my leprosy and I panic... but he treats me not as a leper to be feared and avoided but as a person who needs Him. I know that His power is stronger than this leprosy... and His touch connects me to it. I hear more gasps around me but for Jesus, His only thought is to help me saying,

"I want to. Be clean"... and as I look at my poorly body, I see that the sores have gone. I fall at His feet praising and thanking Him. Jesus wants to heal all of me but he knows there's a part of me that feels lonely and sad because I can't return to my village until I've been passed as healthy. Jesus tells me what to do. He says,

"Go straight to the priest and let Him examine you." I do my part. I go to the priest. He's amazed at my smooth, healthy skin. I tell him all about Jesus. As I run through the village shouting, 'I can come home'... the hugs from my family and friends continue Jesus' work in me... for now I'm being healed of my loneliness and sadness too. Jesus will continue to heal me through my days and nights... and so I live in peace.

You know, what really happened when Jesus touched me was that... instead of me giving Him leprosy... He gave something to me... He gave me a changed body on the outside... and a changed heart on the inside... a heart full of peace and love. Now I try to give Jesus, who lives in me, to others.

PRAYER:

We're going to meet Jesus like the man did.

Put a picture of Jesus into your mind.

See his hand reaching out to touch you with his love and healing power.

Rest with Jesus… just you and him.

Lord it doesn't matter what I'm like inside me or what I look like… your first thought is to help me… the way I am now, in whatever way I need. You want to help me today, tonight and in all my future days and nights.

I welcome your touch...

Come Lord Jesus come. *(say together)*

Amen.

Feeding the Five Thousand

Mark 6: (30-37)

We're always on the move travelling around with Jesus. Today we're all so tired that Jesus says to us, his disciples,

"Let us go off by ourselves to some quiet place where we will be alone and you can rest for a while."
Wearily we drag ourselves into a boat and rest our bodies against the side. The breeze floating across the water cools us. No need to talk… we just sit quietly with Jesus. As the boat gently rocks from side to side some of us fall into a peaceful sleep… others just sit staring into the distance. I'm one of those… I rest with my day-dreams, half awake… half asleep.

Nearing our quiet place, I suddenly see tiny scurrying figures waving to our boat… and all the time the number grows as hundreds hurriedly make their way along the shore-line to our destination. I know they must want to see Jesus.

I look to him… red-rimmed eyes, pale and desperately tired… I just don't know what to do for him as our peace is shattered by the noise reaching us over the water. I wish he could sleep and rest. I see Jesus slowly close his eyes and lower his weary head. His palms face upwards on his lap and I know he talks with the Father.

As he opens his eyes, he looks directly to the people on the shore. I know the father has helped him… his tiredness has been overcome by tremendous love for these people… he looks to them with understanding and welcome.

Stepping firmly onto the shore, his arms spread wide to include everyone. He stands before them like a shepherd and they, the sheep, wait for his guidance… the noise dies to nothing, crying babies turn to sleep, playing children look to him… and Jesus teaches them about the Father's love for them… everyone is still… not a movement… everyone has their eyes on Jesus and his are on them.

As evening falls we say to Jesus, **"It is already late... send the people away... to buy themselves something to eat."**

But as Jesus says, **"You yourselves give them something to eat."** …we realise that if we really cared, we wouldn't send them off for someone else to feed them. We think hard… but it's impossible for us to feed five thousand… we'd need lots of money. We just don't know what to do.

Jesus asks, **"How much bread have you got?"**

As I go off to see, I think, 'I'll do what he wants and find what bread there is but all this seems impossible to me'.

After my frantic search I find a boy with food but ALL I bring back to Jesus is five small loaves and two tiny fish. This seems no use at all but this is all I have. Jesus takes it and smiles at me. He takes the food, holds it high and gives thanks to God... slowly he breaks it and tells us to share it.

I'm confused... how can this small amount possibly feed five thousand... but I do what Jesus wants. My confusion soon turns to amazement as I see that every single person has something to eat. As I weave my way back through the contented crowd, I know I have seen a MIRACLE... and here in my hands I still carry food... more than enough for five thousand people.

As I watch the satisfied people slowly make their way back along the shore, I know they've found what they came looking for today. Jesus has touched their hearts and fed their bodies... He has answered their needs.

Put a picture into your mind of Jesus smiling as He receives just five small loaves and two tiny fish. Now picture the disciples handing out the food to all those people. That's what Jesus did with the tiny offering of food... He made it big... made it great... made it a miracle. Think of someone who you know needed help today... watch Jesus smile at you as you offer and He takes your wish to help that person. Know Jesus is coming to you and making it possible for you to do great things for that person. Jesus is showing His greatness... giving His love through you... and little miracles can happen in our school today.

PRAYER:

Lord, I put my helping spirit into your hands, into your care.

You need it, you want it. You need to use it.

You want to make it great, with your power and love, so that I can be your very special helper.

Come Lord Jesus come *(say together)*...
fill me with your power.
Amen.

The Wise Men

Matthew 2: (1-12)

Every night complete darkness where I live except for the gentle glow of the moon and the twinkling stars. I know these stars well for it's my job to study and learn what they have to tell us. Tonight a new star gradually takes shape before my eyes. It shines brilliantly across the skies. A star of splendour... the king of all stars has been born and I've seen it. I know it tells of a truth here on earth... the truth that a new king... a special king has been born this night and like this star, his light will shine brilliantly across the earth to reach all peoples.

Now, nothing else matters, nothing else seems important but to go off in search of this new king born tonight.

I choose gold, the king of all metals, just right to bring as a gift to a king. I start my journey full of hope and become more excited as I meet others who are on the same journey.

One carries frankincense… the other myrrh… precious gifts for this precious baby.

Night after night we travel by the light of the star. It's a hard journey and we get so weary but we keep each other going in our search.

After many nights travelling we stop to ask where we can find the new king. People just stare at us blankly. Not wanting to give up on our search we go to King Herod and excitedly ask,

"Where is he who has been born king of the Jews? For we have seen his star in the east and have come to worship him."
King Herod is not at all pleased for his eyes look angry and a dark scowl covers his face. His advisors tell him that it was once said that a great king would be born in Bethlehem. King Herod sends us to Bethlehem with these instructions, **"Go and make a careful search for the child and when you find him let me know so that I too may go and worship him."**

…but how can he mean these words for his eyes are hard, cold, unfeeling. Does he try to trick us? Is he afraid the babe will take his kingly-throne from him?

…but towards Bethlehem we turn and there, in the dark skies rests the king of all stars glowing brilliantly down upon the tiny homes of Bethlehem. We know it rests gloriously bright and majestic right over the place where the babe lies.

Dusting ourselves down we quietly enter the place. There before us lies a babe nestled in a poor manger. At this moment I know that this babe before my eyes is the new king... the king of love come to us all... and I seem to breathe in a peace... a peace that fills me... a peace I've never known before.

We fall to our knees in honour of him and I say to him,
"All my wealth is forgotten as I bow low to honour your wealth of true love...
All my power is forgotten as I humbly kneel before the power of your love...
All my knowledge is forgotten as I rest in the knowledge of your glorious birth."

We worship this babe who lies before us in the manger. We worship and praise him for who he is.

As we hear him stir we raise our eyes to him... we give him the best we have... we humbly present him with our gifts... gifts fit for the king of all kings.

PRAYER:

Lord, the Wise Men showed us how determined they were to find you. They found the true wealth of your love.

Lord, the things I own and use don't last long... fill me with the wealth of your love that goes on forever and ever.

Come Lord Jesus come *(together)*

Lord, the Wise Men didn't let anyone stop them getting to you.

Sometimes the power of my friends and the power of my wrong attitude draws me away from you.

Fill me with your power to help me to be strong so that I choose you.

Come Lord Jesus come *(together)*

Lord, the Wise Men wanted to know you more.

Sometimes I think that I know best.

Fill me with knowledge of you... let me know you more so that I do things your way.

Come Lord Jesus come *(together)*

Cleansing the Temple

Matthew 21: (12-14)

This year I'm going up to the temple with my family, for the very first time. I'll be joining hundreds of people who want to worship and thank God for rescuing and freeing his people when they were unhappy and were treated badly. As we reach the temple I'm surprised... it's so noisy and busy. I thought it'd be quiet and calm where people could pray peacefully.

We make our way towards the dove-sellers to buy a dove for our offering. The sellers are all shouting each other down as they try to get us to buy from them. I grip my father's hand feeling unsure of myself... I don't want to get lost in this crowd. They pull on my father's robes trying to draw him to their stalls... but we've never known doves to be as expensive as any of these. My father gets upset... but he starts to carefully count out his coins to pay for a dove, saying that we'll have to do without so many things at home for a long, long time. Near me, I can hear people begging the sellers to drop the price of their doves... but the sellers shout back that they'll have to pay up. I'm not used to all this shouting and it upsets me. Some people get annoyed at the high prices and argue with the sellers, whilst others get upset and have to go home because they just can't pay all that money. I feel sad for those people. I didn't expect this in God's house. There's the clinking of coins all over the place and so much noise and confusion that I don't feel very happy here.

We've brought money so that the temple can be kept in good order but we have to change it into the right coins first. I see the money-changers pointing angry fingers at people. ...hear them shouting and waving their fist on high at people... hear people shouting back at them and this makes me nervous because it's our turn next. As my father hands over his money he's told he has to pay a huge amount of money to get his coins changed. As I wonder why this should be, I see him go white and I know why... he just can't pay all that extra money. He sinks to the floor and holds his head in his hands. As I try to work out what we're going to do, I hear to the right of me... immense rushing and flapping of birds' wings... feathers clouding the air... hundreds of doves blasting out their cries of fear and sellers darting backwards, away from the ferocity of THE ONE who rushes towards them, grabbing their stools and furiously turning them over and crashing them to the ground.

With speed this man's angry eyes flash across to the money-changers. With purpose and determination he strides towards them. With force and strength he hoists their tables high into the air... and as they fall, cascades of coins clatter and crash to the ground... rolling and spreading beneath his feet. The money-changers gasp in horror. Some scramble around scooping coins towards themselves... trying to bury them deep in the pockets of their robes. Everyone's eyes are on this man as His arm sweeps across the chaos before Him. He shakes His head in sadness as He speaks a truth,

"It is written, 'My house shall be a house of prayer'..." And I know that this man is Jesus who speaks the words that God spoke to His children many years ago... and all those here today know these words... but Jesus sees what they have done to this house of prayer and he blasts out another truth to them, **..."but you make it a den of robbers."** ...Jesus understands what we and others have been through today... our hurt and upset has touched His heart... I know that Jesus was right to be angry... Jesus was justified in His anger for...

He found it impossible to stand by and watch... poor people like us being cheated out of our money... He found it impossible to stand by and watch... poor people being made to feel unwelcome and being turned away from God's house of prayer just because they could not pay... He found it impossible to stand by and watch... this reverent house of prayer being turned into a dishonest, disrespectful, market place, which gave no welcome to new worshippers... and at the truth of His words... **"a den of robbers"**... many turn and slink away knowing what they have done wrong... but the honest stall-holders stay to thank Jesus... and He calmly sits with them... helping them... and the poor come to thank Jesus... and new worshippers come to thank Jesus... and He calmly shows them love and acceptance and welcomes them into the temple to pray.

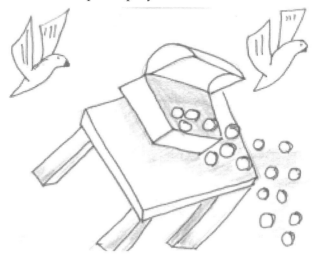

PRAYER:

Today we're going to think of the times when we haven't followed Jesus' example... when we've just stood by and watched someone being hurt in the playground.

Lord, I am sorry.

I'm sorry for the times when I've stood by and watched children criticising other children's clothes and toys.

Lord, I am sorry.

I'm sorry when I've understood how upset another child is and I've just stood by and watched him hurting.

Lord, I am sorry.

I'm sorry for the times when I've stood by and watched myself hurt another child. Lord, I am truly sorry. Amen.

The Widow's Mite

Luke 21: (1–4)

The temple is big and beautiful. We always bring some money to put into the big money boxes so that the temple can be kept special for God.

As I shuffle along in the queue to the money box people in front and behind me chat quietly. I don't know them. They come from the other side of town.

I can hear the tinkle of many coins falling into the box. I wish I had more money to give. I wonder hard. Is there anything else I can go without so that I would have extra coins to give for the temple? I know there isn't. My husband is dead so I rarely have enough money for food and clothes.

Many of the people here have fine clothes. Mine are old and worn but I don't mind because I keep them clean and tidy. I hear the people talk about the fine meals they have but my meals are always plain and ordinary. I don't mind because I love mealtimes. There isn't much food to share out but I always share my friendship and laughter.

I'm nearly to the front of the queue now. The man in front of me is dropping his coins in one by one and has been there ages. He must be a very kind man. Oh how I'd love to have more to offer but I just can't do it. I haven't got anymore money.

At last it's my turn. I won't be here long. I quickly hold my hand over the box and quietly let my two coins fall... and I say, "God, this is all I have today but it's for you. I want you to have it all."

As I turn to make my way down the temple I see Jesus looking at me...and on His face He carries a look of gratitude and understanding but I don't know why. I smile at Him and continue on my way.

Then I hear Him call His disciples to Him and He starts to teach them something that He wants all of you to hear too He says, **"I tell you that this poor widow put in more than all the others... she, as poor as she is, gave all she had to live on."**

Jesus was trying to explain to the disciples that it wasn't the amount of money given that mattered. You see, what I gave was tiny but it was everything I had. So Jesus understood it was a lot for me to give. What others gave was a lot more than me but they had plenty more left for themselves so they only gave a tiny bit of what they had.

Jesus looked into my heart and knew I gave all I could. From my heart I gave all I could even though in my hand it looked small.

After I heard Jesus say all this I now understand that He isn't just talking about money. He wants us to understand that it's about giving to others and not saving things just for ourselves...

... giving and sharing all my friendship...
... giving and sharing all my care...
... giving and sharing all my time...
... giving and sharing all my laughter...
... giving and sharing all my understanding...
... giving and sharing all my love,
     God's love living in me......
.... giving and sharing everything that's in me.

God gave us all these good qualities. He wants us to give them to others and not keep them locked away in our hearts. I understand that when I give all I can He is helping me to do it... and my heart isn't left empty but it gets filled with a joy that being a meany can never give.

I won't feel sad anymore when I see people putting lots of money into the money box. I just need to be honest about it in my heart and ask myself, "Is this the best I can give today?"

PRAYER:

Lord, as I sit with you please come to me through your Spirit to help me to remember to give my best, to practice giving my best and to remember that you are there to help me do it.

Come Lord Jesus come *(together)*
Let us sit quietly as we call on Jesus...
let us rest in His presence...
Amen.

Healing the Paralytic

Mark 2: (2-5)

The heat of the sun is beating down on me as I'm carried on a stretcher. My four friends who are lifting my heavy weight are weak with the effort.

Now and again one of them catches his foot in a hole on the uneven and dusty path to the village and I think they're going to drop me. You know, they've always helped me because I can't do anything for myself... I just can't walk or get around. Now, they're determined to get me into the village and have talked about this for ages. They want me to go to see Jesus.

As we get near the house where Jesus is, we forget about the hard journey. We get all excited but suddenly my friends stop and I'm jerked around on the stretcher... 'What's the matter?' I ask. They say, 'Look'. As I turn my head to look I think...

'Oh no, there's no way we can get in there. There are people outside blocking the doorway. It must be so full in there'.

My heart sinks. I feel for my four friends. They've made so much effort to get me here… but suddenly and with speed I'm being carried towards the crowd. I hear one of them say to me… 'You really need to see Jesus. You really need Jesus to help you. We're determined to get you to him. This crowd is in our way but we're NOT going to let it STOP US. Nothing will stop us getting to Jesus. We're not giving up.'

I know how much they care for me but never realised how much until… with such care they struggle to carry me up the outer staircase of the house. I hold my breath and grip the stretcher so hard as it tilts upwards... but why, why am I now on the roof?

I don't have time to think anymore because I'm shocked at what they start to do next. They seem to be pulling the roof apart. I frantically shout at them to stop. What can they be thinking? You can't go around taking peoples' roofs apart… but they just carry on. The hole gets bigger… dust is flying all over me… and then, … then bits of roof… plaster... dust... start to fall into the house… and the hole gets bigger still.

Through the fog of dust in the house I see a blanket of faces staring up at me. I hear gasps of shock… see some furious glances… some amazed glances… and I stare, eyes wide at others who are rushing and scurrying out of the house away from the falling debris as if the sky will be next to fall in on them.

Then in the middle of them all I see a face chuckling as if amused at the mess and noise they're making… but at the same time a face which seems to take them seriously… this face, the face of Jesus watches intently as my friends carefully lower me through the hole, into the room and right to Jesus' feet.

Silence falls in the room. Jesus raises his head from me to look at my friends and he seems to chuckle again… they must look a right mess, covered in dirt and dust as they peer through the hole in someone's roof.

Then, for a long time he keeps his eyes on them. It's as if Jesus is reading their faces, their eyes… and by doing that he sees their trust in him, their faith in him, their knowing that he will help me… Jesus smiles at them and slightly nods his head as if saying, 'Yes, because you believe it will happen'.

My friends have not given thought to themselves but to me and now, when they have done all they can for me they know Jesus will take over. And He says, **"My son, your sins are forgiven."** …and my heart is full of peace… and he tells me, **"Get up and pick up your mat and walk."** I feel my body tingle. Feeling comes back into my legs… and before I know it, I'm standing, I'm carrying my stretcher and I'm walking… and he's healed me… I have healing forgiveness in my heart... healing strength in my body... healing joy in my mind. Jesus has done this for me.

As I turn the people, amazed at what they have seen, make a path for me through the crowd. I hear them say they've never seen anything like... because what they've seen is Jesus' power to forgive wrongdoing and to heal... all happening before their very eyes.

PRAYER:
Lord I've seen what you've done for the poorly man.
Lord, I believe you can heal me in my heart with your forgiveness.
I believe you can heal my body from its hurts.
I believe you can heal my 'meany' thoughts.
Lord I bring all my friends to you and I come to you Lord Jesus.
Come Lord Jesus come, fill us with your Spirit...
(say together) Amen.

Jesus Forgives a Woman
(the stoning)

John 8: (1–11)

She tries to hide her face... for she did wrong... big wrong. Raised voices around her remind her of what is to become of her. Strong, large men push and shove her from side to side... jeering and shouting about her wrongdoing... until finally their strength overcomes her and her body slides to the ground.

With hands and arms grazed, she raises herself slightly to see long, menacing fingers pointing at her... and there's no escape. She tries to stagger to her feet but stops... rigid in horror she hears,

"In our law this woman must be stoned to death"...
Slowly her head turns and she sees excited, beady eyes glaring into her. She sees their nodding looks of disapproval. As the word 'stoning' echoes around her mind

her eyes fly open and her body freezes in readiness for the first throw of stone... the first pain of stone hitting the body.

Then she sees a different look on just one man's face... not a look of disgust but a look of understanding and sympathy ...not a hand held high clutching a stone but a welcoming hand held out to her... not an uncaring attitude but an attitude of wanting to help.... not a wish to punish but a wish to mend the wrongdoing.... and it's all from Jesus... and the crowd directly asks him,

"What do you say?"....about the stoning. He lowers his head... sadness shaking his body... he looks to the ground running his finger through the dust... and he knows they try to trap him. They expect Jesus to think like they do; ...that He'll either agree to the law of punishment by stoning... or... that He'll disobey the law and just forgive the woman as if her wrongdoing didn't matter.

But Jesus does not think like that... as the Lord of love and forgiveness, he does not punish... as the Son of God, he is not disobedient to the law... and as he traces his fingers in the dust, his body tenses. He knows they don't care about the woman... they just try to trick him.

But, Jesus does not choose their way of thinking... their way of doing things. He chooses the Father's way... he does not disobey the law for he straightens himself up and says to them,

"Whichever one of you has committed no sin...may throw the first stone at her."
Looks of shock spread over their faces... not expecting this, they start to lower their heads, shuffle their feet, discomfort filling the air... they all remember their wrongdoings... all remember their wrong desires and wishes... silence and stillness falls over the crowd.

One of them guiltily turns away and with shoulders rounded and head bent low, he quietly creeps away... and others follow, till not one of them remains... for they now understand that they are not perfect and they make mistakes too... and all have gone, except for the one who has no sin... and that is Jesus.

As she still stands there, Jesus asks her where they all are and if there's anyone left to throw stones at her... and she answers,

"No-one Sir" ...and he does not do what they thought he'd do... to forgive her just as if what she did does not matter for he says strongly and firmly,

"Go but do not sin again."
...and she knows that to be forgiven means that she has to try hard... she has to decide to make a new start and to go and improve her behaviour... and she is happy because she knows Jesus will be with her, helping her to change, to become new.

PRAYER:

This is your special time with Jesus... put a picture of him into your mind and just be with him.

Dear Jesus, I make mistakes too and I am sorry.
Thank you for giving me another chance to change and make a new start.
Come Lord Jesus come.... *(say it together)*
....come and help me to grow in goodness.

We thank and praise you Lord.   Amen.

The Widow's Son

Luke 7: (11–17)

Sadness and grief fill the air as the townspeople follow behind the funeral bier of a young man. His mother, desperately sad at her husband's death, now suffers the loss of her very dear son too. As she follows behind the bier she sees nothing from her empty looking eyes, blurred by tears... not the stones cutting into her feet... not the people moving aside for her. She hears nothing... not my gentle words of understanding... not even the joyful song of the birds. All she knows is deep sadness because she misses her precious son.

Suddenly she staggers... unable to uphold herself... unable to carry the weight of her sadness. She sinks to the ground... the sun sparkles on each tear-drop as it courses over her face only to fade as the tears drop onto the dry dust before her. I rush to her side... helping her to her feet and there before me I see her loneliness... surrounded by people but wanting and needing none... only her beloved son.

I notice a man, followed by a group of people, coming close by us. The man looks to this mother. He looks into her face... into her gushing tearful eyes... and his face shows he understands her sadness. He slowly approaches her... not once taking his eyes from her. This man, this stranger, seems to breathe peace out towards her... for despite her friends' failed attempts to comfort her, it is to this man that she responds...

As he approaches her... she senses his compassion, his understanding... and she turns to look at him...

As he touches her arm... she senses his love... and she reaches out a hand towards him...

As he says, **"Do not cry"**... she senses his love... and she calms and rests in his comforting arms...

As she slowly turns to continue her journey behind the funeral bier of her son, she is aware of this man walking purposefully ahead of her... but she stops... everyone stops... for there he stands... this man, with his hands stretched out towards the bier. We hold our breath and question who he can be... the one who now rests his hands on the bier..?

And as he commands, **"Young man, I say to you get up"** ... she senses his authority... and she waits... and in her waiting, she sees this man's healing power working before her, for...

...her son rises slowly into a sitting position... he turns to this man and they talk... smiling at each other all the time... and in shock she sways... people rush to steady her... her eyes now shining wide with joy, pour out tears of happiness. And as he guides her son through the wildly frightened but amazed crowd towards his mother, she knows that,

"God has visited his people" ... that the God of compassion saw her hurt... came straight into the middle of that hurt... understood that hurt and brought her through that hurt.

And all the people tremble at the wonder they've just seen. They give praise for the glory before them, saying that God has truly come to help and save. And there stands their helper and saviour, hand in hand with mother and son, united in his peace.

PRAYER:

Close your eyes... think of a hurt... a sadness... an upset you've had this week...

remember how you couldn't think of anything else but that hurt...

Put a picture of Jesus into your mind... see Jesus walking towards you as you hurt... just rest and let Jesus do and give you what you need... slowly breathe in the name of Jesus... breathe in what He is wanting to give to you...

Maybe He stretches His arm out to you and takes hold of your hand... Maybe He says, 'Don't be upset'... 'I'm here with you'... 'I understand'...

Jesus is with you... He comes to help you... to be with you... to care for you... and through His healing power He makes it right for you...

Come Lord Jesus come *(together)*
We praise and thank you Lord... Amen.

The Resurrection.
Jesus Appears to Mary Magdalene

John 20: (1-18)

…and all Mary Magdalene can think about… all she sees in her mind, over and over again, are pictures of Jesus… Jesus staggering under the weight of the cross… Jesus suffering tremendous pain on the cross… Jesus being wrapped and laid in the tomb… and she cries,

"Why did this happen to you? Why did they do it to you when all you did was love? You forgave me when everyone else gave up on me and now I'm lost and unhappy without you."

Mary finds herself stumbling towards the tomb. Nothing else matters to her but to be near where Jesus lies. In shock she stares at the tomb… unable to move… a statue of fear… she turns and wildly runs back to find Peter… crying out her upset, "The stone has been rolled away".

Peter and another disciple run straight to the tomb... the younger one looks into the empty tomb and trembling all over, he calls, "Jesus is gone. Who could have done this... why... when did it happen? He suffered so much but now this has happened to Him as well".

...and his head spins and his legs give way with shock. Peter, arriving at the tomb, dashes right past the disciple straight into the tomb crying, "What's happened? What's happened?"

He moves his head left to right, left to right along the length of the place where he knew Jesus had lain. The younger disciple slowly enters the tomb to stand alongside Peter... for long they are silent... just staring... taking in what they see... see with their own eyes... for there before them lie only the cloths that were lovingly placed around Jesus after His death... and Peter exclaims, "Jesus can't have been unwrapped... these cloths lie as they were before... with the same folds... and in the very same place."

Suddenly, the younger disciple grabs hold of Peter saying, "Peter, everything's going to be well again". Peter looks at him questioningly, not understanding what's come over this young disciple beside him and who then shouts, "I've always believed in Jesus and now I believe that God is at work here... Jesus has been freed from the cloths that held Him in this dark tomb... there's hope Peter... Peter there's hope yet".

...and Mary returns to the tomb bending low to look into the tomb. There through her tears, she sees the glowing shapes of two angels who look at her with kindness and understanding. Gently they say,

"Woman why are you crying?" Mary stares, trembling all over as she cries,

"They have taken my Lord away and I do not know where they have put Him." ...and all her hurt and pain flows out to them... "My dear Lord is not here... the tomb is empty... there's just emptiness and darkness like the emptiness and darkness inside me these last few days." The angels wait with Mary as she hurts... as she cries... and Mary is comforted by their presence. Eventually, Mary turns to see a man standing in the garden... just standing and watching her... and he says to her,

"Woman why are you crying?" ...but in her upset she does not recognise that these words are the very same words that God's angels spoke. He asks her,

"Who is it that you are looking for?" Mary, looking through eyes misted with tears thinks she sees the gardener... and feeling warmed by his concern, she tells him all about Jesus and says,

"If you took Him away sir, tell me where you have put Him and I will go and get Him"...and for a long time He looks to Mary whilst Mary sinks to the ground, holds her head in her hands and sobs out her grief and He sees and knows of Mary's deep love. As if from away in the distance, she hears her name… just her name…

"Mary" …and she hears it spoken with understanding… with tenderness…
"Mary"…and as that one word echoes round her mind… she knows it comes with huge, huge love…
"Mary"…and as that one word fills her mind… she senses the presence of Jesus…

…and Mary, calls to Jesus by His name…
"Jesus" …and as she calls His name, just His name… she swells in belief that this man before her is Jesus… Jesus alive… alive in a new way. And Mary rejoices.

PRAYER:
See yourself standing with Mary in front of Jesus…Jesus asks Mary why she's upset…why she's crying. He asks you too…tell Jesus how you are…how you feel…

Jesus calls Mary's name… hear Him call your name… the name of His beloved child… your special name. He's welcoming you… wanting you to come to Him… He wants to give you His help… His strength… His love. Come Lord Jesus come (*together*).

Just sit quietly with Jesus… let Him give you what you need. Come lord Jesus come (*together*).   Amen.

Gethsemane/The Passion

Note: The last, extended, meditation - Gethsemane/The Passion - is used as a play and is suitable for Primary age children. Background music: Adagio in G minor. Albinoni/Giazotto. During the narrator's readings (usually the teacher or catechist), the children stand in prayer

...and after the Last Supper, Jesus walked with His disciples... He went to a quiet place up on the slopes of a hill... and the gentle breeze whispered through the grasses... small flowers danced and waved... and Jesus walked through his garden together with his disciples. He knew He faced pain, agonising pain and hurt... and in His need it was to ABBA... FATHER He came. He turned to you, His disciples, and said,

"Sit here while I go over there and pray." ...and taking three disciples with Him He slowly moved further into the garden... His head hung low... His shoulders drooped. Jesus always helped and cared for others... was always strong... always knowing what to do... what to say... but now His mind swelled ,with agonising thoughts... agonising fears... and His disciples did not understand this change in Him and He said to them,

"The sorrow in my heart is so great that it almost crushes me. Stay here and keep watch."

(Sing: Taize 'Stay with me and keep watch with me')

and in His deep upset He threw Himself down to the ground... strength flowed out of Him... fear flowed into Him... and lovingly... and desperately, He called to the one who would help Him... the one who was true father to Him... the one who loved Him... the one who wouldn't let Him down... and He prayed,

"Abba, my Father all things are possible for you. Take this *(cup of)* **suffering away from me. Yet not what I want but what you want,"** and His face... His face was grey and lined with pain... His eyes, red-rimmed and lifeless as He turned to find His disciples asleep... and how He needed them... how He wanted them just to be there... there WITH HIM while He hurt... there without words, without actions... just there ...and sadly He said,

"How is it that you three were not able to keep watch with me even for one hour?"

(Sing: Taize 'Stay with me and keep watch with me')

and they looked at Jesus... not knowing what to say to Him... and in the peace of the garden... there they gave in to sleep... they slept the sleep of the exhausted... not understanding that He was hurting... that He wanted them to be with Him... not understanding what was to come... not understanding that He faced the cross.

Jesus turned to pray... alone... isolated... churning with fear... His mind torn apart, scattering the seeds of sleep... and there in His weakness He prayed.

His body trembled... His eyes appealed... sweat gathered in pools around Him... He hurt worse than any one of us will ever hurt...

and in torment He begged the Father... pleaded with Abba, Father, that maybe there was another way for Him other than the cross...

and Abba Father, saw the pain He went through... heard His cries for help... held Him... cherished Him... and sent the angel of comfort to strengthen Him... His own beloved son... to strengthen Him to do what he wanted Him to do.

and Jesus knew that Abba... his loving Father... wanted Him to go forward... to do His will... forward towards the cross... and He stood tall and straight...

NARRATOR:

You are Jesus. We are here with you in the garden at Gethsemane. You know that you are facing death. You feel alone. Your friends are asleep. You are human like us and don't want this hurt but... you do not run from it. You pray and pray and pray.

You believe the Father wants you to carry on. You believe He will help you. Dear Jesus we're sad that you're hurting in the garden. Your hurt is bigger than any of our hurts, so you always know how we feel. We thank you Jesus... we're sorry when we haven't been your friend. Help us to have courage to go through hard times like you do here. Help us to trust like you do so that we do the Father's will when it seems too hard for us.

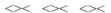

A loud noise was heard.
Soldiers were marching to take Jesus away.
Jesus and His friends watched them.
They came to Jesus.

Now full of courage... full of strength... He turned to His disciples saying,

"Look, here is the man who is betraying me..."
And as the one who was to betray Him approached... the soldiers watched closely for they knew the one to be kissed would be Jesus... the one they were searching for would be betrayed with the sign of a kiss.

The soldiers said,
"Are you the man we want?"
"Are you the man we want?"
"Are you the man we want?"
Jesus said, **"I am He."**
The soldiers took Jesus away. He was put into prison. There were some people who did not understand Jesus. They did not understand how good He was.

They said,
"He is to die."
"He is to die."
"He is to die."

How sad Jesus' friends were. How afraid they were for Him.

NARRATOR:
You are Jesus. We are here with you as the soldiers come for you. You say, "I am He"... you could have denied it... but you said it because you are truth. You could have walked away but you stayed... you chose the Father's will for you.

We see you there alone, no weapons, facing an army shining with weapons and armour. We see you taken away. You walk tall with the authority of one who knows that He does the Father's will.

There you stand, hearing them scream AGAINST you...
not FOR you, our King of Peace. They scream to harm
you. They choose hurt over peace.

Dear Jesus, it's hard to watch what's happening to you...
you the innocent one. You who do nothing but love,
being treated so badly... but your courage shines through
...your obedience to the Father shines through.

We thank you for doing this for us. We're sorry when
we've not chosen to do things your way but our own way
by hurting others and ourselves. Help us not to hurt you
more by hurting others. Help us to love you by choosing
your path of peace.

Jesus was given a big heavy cross to carry
He was tired. He was hot. He was thirsty.
Jesus fell.
The soldiers made Him get up.
Jesus fell again.
Mary came to Jesus. She was unhappy to see Him hurting.

(Sing: Mary's song)

Jesus was getting more tired.
He fell again. Simon helped Him.

NARRATOR:

This is you, Jesus. We see the enormous weight of the cross being placed on your back. The thorns dig into your head and cut your skin. We see you stagger, exhausted, until you fall. Your face becomes pale and streamed with sweat. Your back bleeds, yet you remain silent. You don't complain. You don't profess your innocence. You remain obedient to the Father's will and the Father wants you to do this for us. We see Simon help you with your cross when, being human like us, you could bear it no more.

Dear Lord, as we look at you we're saddened by your suffering. From our hearts we say thank you for doing this for us. Please help us to love others like you love us. Help us to love our friends when they have a hard time, like Simon helped you in your hard time.

Jesus was taken to a lonely hill. All his friends were sad. Jesus said:

"Forgive them. They do not know what they have done."

He cried out,

"Father, I put myself into your hands."

With that, Jesus hung His head and died.

(Sing: Jesus, remember me when you come into your kingdom)

141

NARRATOR:
This is Jesus true God and true man. As we see you on the cross we see your sore skin, your paleness and your wounds. Despite this you look out and away from yourself. Your look is of love as you slowly move your eyes to both those who love and care for you and to the uncaring ones around your cross.

As we see pain travel through your body, we know how tremendous is your love for us. There is nothing you wouldn't do for us to show us your love and forgiveness. there is no suffering we could have that you haven't had already.

...and as you give your Spirit into the Father's hands, you show us how you are one with the Father.

Lord Jesus, how sorry we are for your pain and suffering. We thank you for going through this for us. We thank you for your forgiveness. Please help me to do your will... to choose your loving way that goes out to every-one forever instead of my selfish way that goes inwards and is just for me.

(Sing: Mary's song)

Further copies of this book
are available from

Goodnews Books & Resources
St. John the Apostle Church Buildings
296 Sundon Park Road
Luton, Beds. LU3 3AL

+44 01582 571011
www.goodnewsbooks.net
orders@goodnewsbooks.net